The Open University

Science: a second level course

Astronomy

and

Planetary Science

Book 3

Galaxies

Book chair: Barrie Jones

Prepared for the Course Team by
Dave Adams, Barrie Jones, Bob Lambourne, Liz Swinbank

The Open University

S281 Course Team
Course Team Chair and General Editor Barrie Jones
Block 1 Chair Barrie Jones
Block 2 Chair Dave Rothery
Block 3 Chairs Barrie Jones and Bob Lambourne
Block 4 Chair Russell Stannard
Course Manager Cheryl Newport

Dave Adams *University of Leicester* (Author)
Jocelyn Bell Burnell (Author)
Cameron Balbirnie (BBC Producer)
Giles Clark (Publishing)
Alan Cooper (AV Production)
Sue Dobson (Graphic Artist)
Carol Forward (Course Secretary)
Peter Francis (Author)
John Greenwood (Library)
Charlie Harding (Author)
Karen Hill (Author)
Jonathan Hunt (Publishing)
Tony Jolly (BBC Series Producer)
Barrie Jones (Author)
Robert Lambourne (Author)
Jean McCloughry (Staff Tutor)
Elaine Moore (Author)
Lesley Passey (Designer)
Colin Pillinger (Author)
Ian Robson *University of Central Lancashire* (Author)
Dave Rothery (Author)
Dick Sharp (Editor)
Russell Stannard (Author)
Liz Swinbank (Consultant)
Margaret Swithenby (Editor)
Arnold Wolfendale *University of Durham* (Course Assessor)
Ian Wright (Author)
John Zarnecki *University of Kent* (Author)

Cover: The image of Centaurus A, the nearest active galaxy, at visible wavelengths. Courtesy of Anglo Australian Telescope Board. Photograph by David Malin.

The Open University, Walton Hall, Milton Keynes, MK7 6AA.
First published 1994
Edited, designed and typeset by The Open University.
Printed in the United Kingdom by Henry Ling Ltd., at the Dorset Press, Dorchester, Dorset
ISBN 0 7492 51271
This text forms part of an Open University Second Level Course. If you would like a copy of *Studying with The Open University*, please write to the Central Enquiry Service, PO Box 200, The Open University, Walton Hall, Milton Keynes, MK7 6YZ. If you have not enrolled on the Course and would like to buy this or other Open University material, please write to Open University Educational Enterprises Ltd, 12 Cofferidge Close, Stony Stratford, Milton Keynes, MK11 1BY, United Kingdom.
1.1

Book 3 Galaxies

Contents

Introduction and study guide for Block 3

Block 3, *Galaxies*, deals with one of astronomy's most exciting frontiers. New telescopes and new detectors have increased our knowledge of galaxies enormously over the last few years and, thanks to major initiatives such as the Hubble Space Telescope, this explosive development shows every sign of continuing. However, even with this wealth of observational data our understanding of galaxies is still far from complete, and if this Block seems to contain a larger number of imponderables than earlier parts of the Course, then that is a fair reflection of the current state of the subject.

The text of the book is divided into four chapters. The first deals with the galaxy in which we live – the Milky Way. This is the domain of the subject usually referred to as 'galactic astronomy'. Chapters 2 and 3 extend the discussion into the field of 'extra-galactic astronomy' by considering galaxies beyond the Milky Way. Chapter 2 is concerned with so-called *normal galaxies*, which have a more or less constant luminosity that can be roughly accounted for in terms of the known stars and gas that the galaxy contains. Chapter 3 deals with the more enigmatic *active galaxies*, which exhibit features such as unusually high and highly variable luminosity, and which often show signs of exotic behaviour in their centres. The fourth and final chapter is much shorter than the others. It describes the distribution of galaxies throughout space and thus provides an overview of the large-scale structure of the Universe. This area of study, which has revealed the largest known structures in the Universe, has made particularly rapid progress in recent years and is certain to be the focus of fascinating future developments.

The text of this book is supported by two TV programmes, four video sequences and an audio band. TV programme 6, *Mapping the Milky Way*, accompanies Chapter 1 and is concerned with the thorny problem of determining the overall structure of the Milky Way. Video sequence 9, *Galactic spiral density waves*, also relates to Chapter 1, and deals with the spiral arms of the Milky Way. Video sequence 10, *A radioastronomy project*, accompanies Chapter 2, and shows how radio observations are used to study the motion of other spiral galaxies. TV programme 7, *Jets and black holes*, looks at the highly detailed studies of active galaxies, the subject of Chapter 3. The audio band (audio band 3) also relates to Chapter 3 and is concerned with the spectra of active galaxies. Video sequences 11 and 12, *Galaxies in space* and *Interacting galaxies*, should be viewed when you reach the end of the book – sequence 11 deals with the distribution of galaxies in space, which is the subject of Chapter 4, and sequence 12 looks at interactions between galaxies.

Chapter 1
The Milky Way – our galaxy

Prepared for the Course Team by Bob Lambourne and Liz Swinbank

Contents

1.1 Introduction

The term 'Milky Way' is used by astronomers in two distinct senses. On the one hand it indicates the faint band of light that arches across the night sky from horizon to horizon (Figure 1.1 and Plate 3.3). On the other hand, it is used as the name of our own galaxy – a vast astronomical system that includes about 10^{11} stars, one of which is the Sun. This latter use predominates here.

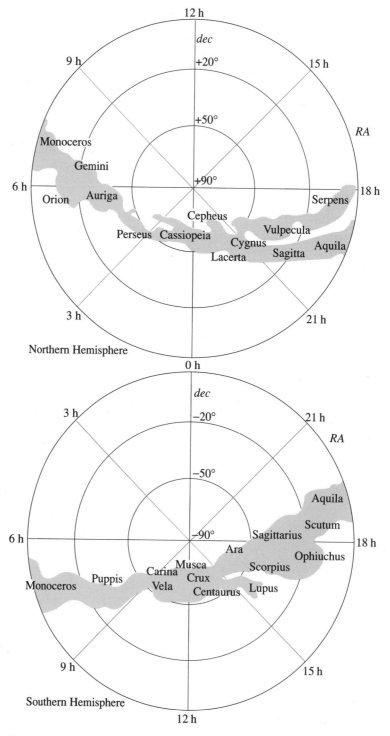

Figure 1.1 The faint irregular band of the Milky Way arches across the night sky, passing through a circle of constellations.

Of course, the two meanings of the term are not entirely disconnected. Soon after Galileo Galilei first started to use a telescope to make astronomical observations, around 1610, he discerned that the pale band of the Milky Way is composed of countless stars. This is now recognized as clear evidence that the Sun is located within a thin disc of stars, which is itself one of the major structural components of the Milky Way galaxy. Describing this *disc* of stars, together with the other major **structural components** – the *nuclear bulge* at its centre, and the *halo* in which the disc and bulge are embedded – is the major aim of this chapter.

The text of the chapter is divided into four major sections. The first provides an overview of the Milky Way that includes an introduction to the major components (disc, bulge and halo) and a guide to the main constituents (stars, gas, dust, etc.) making up those components. The remaining three sections look in greater detail at, respectively, the disc, the halo and the bulge. These more detailed discussions include accounts of topics such as the pattern of star formation in the disc, the distribution of star clusters in the halo, and the search for a supermassive black hole at the centre of the nuclear bulge.

Chapter 1 is supported by two other components; a TV programme and a video sequence. TV programme 6, *Mapping the Milky Way*, describes some techniques that have been employed to deduce the three-dimensional structure of the Milky Way galaxy from the two-dimensional views available from the Earth. It may be viewed at any stage during your work on this chapter, but relates most closely to Section 1.3. Video sequence 9, *Galactic spiral density waves*, concerns the rotation of the Milky Way and the nature of its spiral arms, and should be viewed as soon as possible after you have finished Subsection 1.3.3.

1.2   An overview of the Milky Way

1.2.1   The size and structure of the Milky Way

The Milky Way is huge; at least 100 000 light years (30 kpc) across, perhaps a good deal more. Ironically, the exact size of our own galaxy is more difficult to determine than that of some of the other galaxies that can be seen far beyond its boundaries. There are a number of reasons for this surprising state of affairs. One is that the outer parts of the Milky Way are relatively dim and hard to define, but this is a difficulty that applies to all galaxies and is, in any case, not the most serious problem. A greater cause of uncertainty is the Milky Way itself. Because we are located *within* the Milky Way's disc, the material of which it is made blocks our view in certain directions whilst leaving others unobscured. This makes some observations difficult or even impossible, particularly those which involve looking out to great distances in the disc. In general, we now use our knowledge of those galaxies that appear to be similar to the Milky Way in order to understand our own galaxy better. Our situation is somewhat akin to that of a motorist trying to describe his or her own car by observing it only from within, and by looking at passing cars on a motorway.

Describing one's own car is difficult, as many vital parts are obscured from view. Describing the cars that can be seen through the windscreen is easier, but the observations need then to be related to one's own car. The motorist might well conclude from the available evidence that his or her own car had four wheels, but even this might be called into question by the sight of a Robin Reliant overtaking in the fast lane.

A third reason for the difficulty of assessing the true size of the Milky Way is that a good deal of it is thought to be made up of so-called **dark matter** that does not emit light or any other kind of radiation that has yet been detected. Dark matter is not merely invisible. Thus, whereas 'ordinary' matter consists largely of

Remember, the parsec (pc) is a unit of astronomical distance equal to about 3.26 light years. Thus, 30 kpc is equivalent to about 98 000 light years. It is conventional to express galactic distances in terms of parsecs and kiloparsecs.

Note that electrons, which are common in ordinary matter, and are not 'exotic', are not actually baryons.

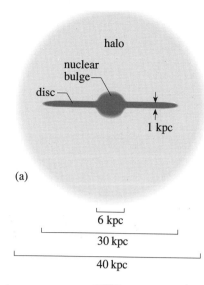

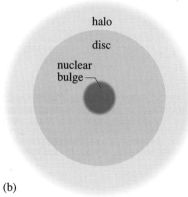

Figure 1.2 (a) Edge-on and (b) face-on views of the major structural components of the Milky Way – the disc, the halo and the nuclear bulge. (In Book 1, Subsection 5.2.4, you learned that, for gas and dust, the disc thickness is about 0.3 kpc.)

baryons (protons, neutrons and related particles) and is often referred to as **baryonic matter**, dark matter is thought likely to consist, at least in part, of other, more exotic, types of particle whose exact nature has yet to be determined. Despite its lack of radiation, the presence of dark matter can be deduced from its gravitational influence on matter that can be seen. Indirect studies of this kind indicate that the total mass of the dark matter associated with the Milky Way is very substantial; perhaps ten times greater than the total mass of directly detectable matter. Nonetheless, the exact nature of the dark matter and the details of its distribution are still unknown. It is assumed that the dark matter forms a sort of cloud enveloping the visible parts of the Milky Way and stretching well beyond them, but the size and shape of this cloud are not currently measurable. We shall have much more to say about dark matter in Chapters 2 and 4 and in Block 4.

Crudely speaking, the directly detectable parts of the Milky Way consist of the three major structural components – the **disc**, the **halo** and the **nuclear bulge** – which are shown schematically in Figure 1.2. This diagram should be compared with Plate 3.1, a medium-exposure photograph of a nearby galaxy, thought to be broadly similar to the Milky Way, which clearly shows a disc and bulge but gives little indication of the halo revealed by more detailed studies.

Figure 1.2 associates particular sizes with the various components but, for the reasons given above, some of these sizes are actually rather poorly determined, so the values quoted should be regarded as rough guides rather than precise measurements. The diameter of the disc has been indicated as 30 kpc, that of the bulge as 6 kpc and that of the halo as 40 kpc, though the last figure is especially crude and some authors would use a value two or three times bigger. The disc is shown as having a thickness of 1 kpc, but this simple figure hides a multitude of sins. Like each of the other components, the disc contains a range of constituents – stars, gas, dust, etc. – and there is no reason to suppose that these different constituents will all be distributed in exactly the same way. Indeed, in the case of the disc there is fairly clear evidence that they are not. In a more precise description of the disc a separate thickness would be associated with each of its constituents. However, in the spirit of this simple overview, we shall just stick to a single thickness, 1 kpc. Additional detail will be given as and when necessary.

The halo and the nuclear bulge are shown in Figure 1.2 as roughly spherical, though they are both thought to be somewhat flattened. They are sometimes treated as a single component, usually referred to as the **Galactic spheroid**. A mild controversy about whether or not the bulge really is a distinct structural component or simply a central concentration of the halo has existed for some time. It is generally rather difficult to disentangle these two components, though there is no doubt about the separateness of the disc since the stars there are younger and move differently from those of the Galactic spheroid. A widespread belief that the Galactic spheroid represents an older part of the Milky Way, within which the disc has evolved, is supported by the existence of very ancient globular clusters in the halo. Globular clusters will be discussed in some detail in Section 1.4. For the present we just note the bare facts that they are compact, dense clusters of very old stars, typically containing 10^5–10^6 members in a spherical region of space less than 50 pc in diameter. The total number of globular clusters associated with the Milky Way is between 150 and 200, and they jointly account for about 1% of all the stars in the halo. The presence of globular clusters is indicated in Plate 3.2 which tries to give a more realistic impression of the Milky Way than Figure 1.2.

Another feature of Plate 3.2 deserves particular emphasis; the presence of **spiral arms** in the disc. Spiral arms are a common feature of galaxies, and Figure 1.3 shows a particularly clear example. The overall spiral shape of the arms is very clear yet, looked at in detail, the arms are actually somewhat fragmented and distorted. The Sun is located close to the mid-plane of the disc, between two major spiral arms and in what may be a fragment or a spur of another spiral arm. Observations indicate that the Sun is about a third of the way in from the edge of the disc, at a distance of 7.5–10 kpc from the centre of the Milky Way. It should be noted that although most of the disc stars seem to be located in the spiral arms, this is not really the case. The spiral arms stand out because they contain unusually *bright* stars, not because they contain unduly large *numbers* of stars. The reasons why bright stars should be concentrated in this way will be discussed in detail in Section 1.3.

Figure 1.3   M101, a galaxy in Ursa Major with prominent spiral arms.

There is some debate as to whether the Milky Way is actually a **barred spiral galaxy**. Plate 3.8d shows a spiral galaxy with a prominent central bar. Observations of other spiral galaxies show that the majority have some trace of a central bar, and computer simulations indicate that the presence of a bar may be associated with stability. However, the central regions of the Milky Way are notoriously difficult to observe and while (as you will see in TV programme 6) there is some observational evidence for a bar, the situation is far from clear.

1.2.2   The constituents of the Milky Way

Now that we have introduced the major structural components of the Milky Way, this is a good point at which to say something about the constituents that make up those components. Apart from dark matter, about which very little is known, the Milky Way is mainly composed of stars, gas and dust. There are thought to be about 10^{11} stars in all, and, since the Sun's mass ($M_\odot = 1.99 \times 10^{30}$ kg) is fairly typical, they are expected to have a combined mass of about $10^{11} M_\odot$. This enormous mass of stars is considered in more detail in Subsection 1.2.3. The total mass of gas is thought to amount to about 10% of the total stellar mass, i.e. about $10^{10} M_\odot$. The nature of the gas has already been discussed in some detail, in

Chapter 5 of Book 1. The main points mentioned there will be reviewed in Subsection 1.2.4 below, but for the present we should note that the gas is roughly 75% hydrogen and 25% helium (by mass), and that the hydrogen may be in the form of molecules (H_2), atoms (H) or ions (H^+), according to local conditions of density, temperature and UV flux. The dust content of the Milky Way was also discussed in Book 1. It consists of particles that are typically 10^{-6}–10^{-7} m across and its total mass is about 0.1% of the stellar mass, i.e. about $10^8\,M_\odot$. Much of the dust is concentrated around the mid-plane of the disc, where it is particularly effective at scattering light. It is this dust that is mainly responsible for the zone of obscuration that limits our ability to make optical observations in the disc, as indicated in Figure 1.4.

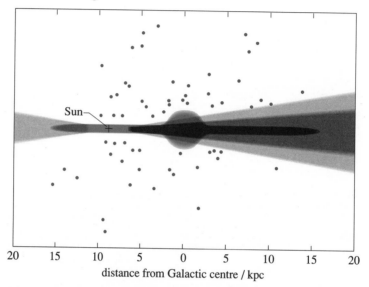

distance from Galactic centre / kpc

Figure 1.4   Due to the presence of dust in the Milky Way's disc, optical observations in the light grey regions are very difficult and those in the dark grey region are essentially impossible, except for *very* bright objects within about 5 kpc.

When referring to the Milky Way, 'Galaxy' and 'Galactic' will be printed with a capital G to distinguish our galaxy from galaxies in general.

The eV (electronvolt) is a unit of energy; $1\,\text{eV} = 1.602 \times 10^{-19}$ J. $1\,\text{MeV} = 10^6\,\text{eV}$.

In addition to stars, gas, dust and dark matter, the Milky Way also contains a number of other constituents that play an important role in determining its nature, even though they contribute little to its overall mass. Perhaps the most significant of these minor constituents are the *cosmic rays* that permeate the Galaxy.

Cosmic rays (Book 1, Section 5.3) are energetic charged particles, with some γ-rays. About 85% of the particles are protons, 12% are helium nuclei, 1% are heavier nuclei and 2% are electrons. Their energies are typically in the range 10^6–10^{20} eV (about 10^{-13}–10 J), and the overall contribution of cosmic rays to the Milky Way is often expressed in terms of their energy density, i.e. the energy in the cosmic rays in a typical unit volume of space. For cosmic rays the energy density is about $1\,\text{MeV}\,\text{m}^{-3}$. The highest-energy cosmic rays come from outside the Milky Way, but those of intermediate energy (10^{10}–10^{16} eV) are thought to originate within the Galaxy. It seems that shock waves from supernovae may be responsible for accelerating particles to these very high energies. Regardless of the source of their energy, however, there can be no doubt that cosmic rays interacting with interstellar gas clouds produce X-rays and γ-rays that make a significant contribution to the Milky Way's total emission of electromagnetic radiation at very short wavelengths (see Plate 3.4d).

A second minor constituent is the **Galactic magnetic field**. Observations indicate that it lies primarily in the disc, mainly aligned with the spiral arms. A magnetic field has energy, and the contribution of the Galactic magnetic field to the energy density of the Milky Way is usually reckoned to be about equal to that of the cosmic rays. Of course, since cosmic rays are charged particles, they will interact with the magnetic field, which will bend their paths. Electrons, the lightest cosmic ray particles, are particularly susceptible to such influences and will consequently give off synchrotron radiation at radio wavelengths. Radiation of this kind makes a significant contribution to the Milky Way's total emission of electromagnetic radiation at long wavelengths (see Plate 3.4a).

Synchrotron radiation was introduced in Subsection 5.2.5 of Book 1.

Electromagnetic radiation in general, from radio waves to γ-rays, is another minor constituent of the Milky Way. Starlight and other visible light travelling within the Galaxy makes a total contribution to the energy density that is about equal to that of the cosmic rays. A similar contribution comes from the microwave part of the spectrum: this is especially large compared with other wavelength ranges because it is boosted by the contribution of the cosmic background radiation, a universal 'gas' of photons thought to be left over from the Big Bang (the early stages of the Universe). (Cosmic background radiation and the Big Bang will be considered in detail in Block 4.)

Finally, mention should be made of neutrinos. You should already be aware from Block 1 that nuclear reactions in stars produce large numbers of neutrinos, which are very difficult to detect. But neutrinos coming from stars are unlikely to make much of a contribution to the overall energy content of the Milky Way. However, it is widely thought that the Universe (including the place where you are now) is permeated by a hitherto undetectable background of neutrinos that originated in the Big Bang along with the cosmic background radiation mentioned above. These cosmic neutrinos simply have too low an energy to be detected with current technology (such 'astronomical' neutrinos as have been detected on Earth originate mainly from the Sun) but their existence is well established by theories of the Big Bang which are themselves supported by observations. If neutrinos had a small but finite mass, then the cosmic neutrino background might be the dominant form of matter in the Universe and might even account for the dark matter in and beyond the Milky Way that was discussed earlier. At the present time this possibility is disfavoured; there is no substantiated experimental evidence to show that neutrinos do have the requisite mass, and computer simulations of an evolving Universe dominated by neutrinos with mass do not produce an outcome that looks anything like our own Universe. Nonetheless, the possibility that neutrinos may be the masters of the Universe is an intriguing one.

1.2.3 The stellar content of the Milky Way

As you saw in Block 1, stars have a wide range of intrinsic properties. Individual stars can differ from one another in their luminosity, their spectral class and in a number of other ways.

The first indication that there might be systematic variations in stellar properties between one region of the Milky Way and another came from observations of M31, the Andromeda Galaxy (Plate 3.8b), made near Los Angeles by the German-born American astronomer Walter Baade (1893–1960), during the wartime blackout of 1943. Although M31 is so far away that Baade was unable to see stars even as luminous as the Sun, he could detect a clear difference between the spectra of the stars in the disc of M31 and those in its nuclear bulge. He named these two broad types **population I** and **population II** respectively.

Subsequent observations within the Milky Way showed that not only was the idea of stellar populations applicable to our own galaxy, but that it needed to be refined to accommodate a greater number of distinct populations, each defined by characteristics such as the average age, metallicity and motion of the stars that it contains. Opinions differ as to the number of different populations that can usefully be identified; we shall limit our discussion to four.

Metallicity was defined in Book 1, Subsection 1.5.3, as the mass of elements heavier than hydrogen and helium as a fraction of the total mass.

Extreme population I

Stars belonging to this population are mainly found in the spiral arms, where they move in essentially circular orbits around the Galactic centre. These are young stars, typically less than 20×10^6 to 50×10^6 years old, with average metallicities of about 3%. Extreme population I objects include short-lived but spectacularly brilliant blueish–white stars of spectral classes O, B1 and B2, T Tauri stars and certain types of supergiant, including high-mass Cepheid variables (those with periods in excess of 10–13 days).

Intermediate population I

These stars also move in circular orbits, but they are found throughout the disc, not just in the spiral arms. They are somewhat older than the extreme population I stars, with typical ages in the range 0.2×10^9 to 10×10^9 years and metallicities of 1–2%. The Sun is a member of this population along with most of the other stars in the visually observable part of the disc.

Intermediate population II

These are old stars with ages in the range 2×10^9 to 10×10^9 years. They have rather low metallicities, typically 0.8% or so. Stars of this population are found in the inner parts of the halo and the nuclear bulge (though the bulge also contains stars with the high metallicities typical of population I). Unlike the stars of the disc, these stars do not have circular orbits, nor are they confined to the plane of the disc. Rather, they move in moderately elliptical orbits, though still centred on the Galactic centre.

Extreme population II

These are the oldest of the stars, with typical ages of 10×10^9 to 14×10^9 years. Their metallicity is very low – usually less than 0.8% – and they are found mainly in the halo, particularly in the ancient globular clusters. Many of these stars move around the Galactic centre in highly elliptical orbits that are often steeply inclined to the disc. Typical members of this population are low-mass stars that have left the main sequence, and RR Lyrae variables (somewhat more massive stars that have evolved onto the horizontal branch of the H–R diagram, see Subsection 3.4.1 of Book 1).

ITQ 1.1 On the basis of what you learned in Book 1, why would you expect that old stars (i.e. stars that formed a long time ago) should have low metallicity?

It is important to realize that since the disc lies within the halo there is a certain degree of intermingling of different star populations. There are no sharp boundaries, but rather, broad regions in which one population gives way to another. Thus, in our part of the disc for instance, which is mainly occupied by population I stars, there are a number of stars that really belong to population II. Since these stars of the Galactic spheroid (i.e. halo and bulge) population are usually following highly elliptical orbits that are quite different from the circular orbits commonly found in the disc, they often have abnormally high velocities relative to the disc stars that surround them. Consequently, such stars are called **high-velocity stars** and may be easily recognized as probable members of an 'alien' population.

Allowing for the different sizes and properties of the various stellar populations, it is possible to estimate the expected relative abundance of each spectral class of star in the Milky Way as a whole. This is shown graphically in Figure 1.5.

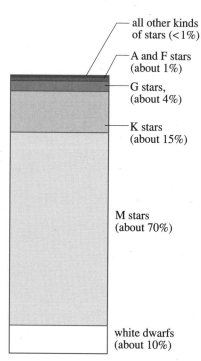

all other kinds of stars (<1%)

A and F stars (about 1%)

G stars, (about 4%)

K stars (about 15%)

M stars (about 70%)

white dwarfs (about 10%)

Figure 1.5 The approximate relative abundances of stars belonging to different spectral classes in the Milky Way as a whole. The Sun is a G star.

1.2.4 The gaseous content of the Milky Way

The gaseous content of the Milky Way is important for a number of reasons. Clearly, since it amounts to about 10% of the stellar mass, it has a certain importance in its own right. Moreover, as you saw in Book 1, the interstellar medium (nearly all of which is gas) is the starting point for star formation and plays a vital part in the recycling of material that enables the Galaxy to evolve chemically, gradually increasing its overall abundance of heavy elements. In addition, as you will see in the next subsection, studies of Galactic gas provide information about the rotation of the Milky Way and hence insight into its total mass. As explained in Chapter 5 of Book 1, the structure of the Milky Way's gaseous content is very complicated. Mapping the distribution of atomic hydrogen (H) using 21 cm radiation has played an important part in deducing that structure. Most of the cold gas is confined to the 1 kpc thick disc, where much of it is further concentrated into a central layer about 0.3 kpc thick. The gas in this thin disc is divided into tens of thousands of clouds enveloped by hot and warm intercloud media. This whole structure is itself embedded in a hot intercloud medium that occupies at least part of the halo, though its precise distribution is far from clear. A summary of the nature and distribution of the interstellar medium (ISM) is provided by Figure 1.6 and Table 1.1, both of which have been reproduced from Chapter 5 of Book 1. Further insight into the average distribution of the various forms of hydrogen – molecular (H_2), atomic (H) and ionized (H^+) – can be obtained from Figure 1.7. Note that the figure treats the gas as a disc and describes the density of each form in terms of a 'column density' expressed in solar masses per square parsec ($M_\odot\,pc^{-2}$). As you can see, the various forms of hydrogen are distributed quite differently.

The origin of 21 cm radiation was explained in Subsection 5.2.1 of Book 1. The use of this radiation in Milky Way studies is a major topic in TV programme 6.

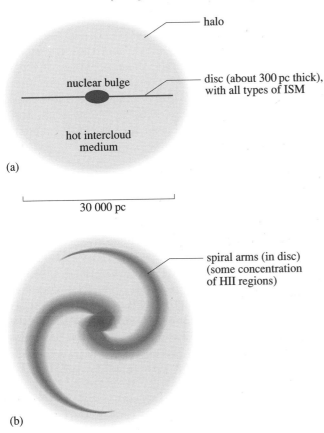

Figure 1.6   The distribution of the gaseous content of the Milky Way. (a) Edge-on view; (b) face-on view.

Table 1.1   Some features of the various types of region in the ISM

Type of region	Fraction of the ISM/% [a]		Typical size/pc [c]	Predominant form of hydrogen	Abundance of molecules
	By volume [b]	By mass			
hot intercloud medium	~ 60	$\lesssim 0.1$	—	H^+	very low
warm intercloud medium	~ 30	~ 20	—	H^+ or H	very low
diffuse clouds	~ 3	~ 30	~ 3 to ~ 100	H or H_2	diatomic molecules common
dense clouds	$\lesssim 1$	~ 45	~ 0.1 to ~ 20	H_2	molecules common, even large ones
HII regions	~ 10	~ 1	~ 1 to ~ 20	H^+	very low
circumstellar shells	negligible	negligible	$\lesssim 1$	H or H_2	diatomic common
planetary nebulae	negligible	negligible	$\lesssim 2$	H^+	very low
supernova remnants	d	negligible	$\lesssim 1\,000$	H^+ or H	very low

[a] These percentages are only rough estimates, so do not sum to 100%.

[b] The total volume of the ISM is taken to be a disc with a diameter roughly that of the spiral arms of the Milky Way, i.e. 30 000 pc, and a thickness of 300 pc.

[c] These are typical distances across a region, such that the volume $V \sim \frac{4}{3}\pi\,(\text{size}\,/2)^3$. For roughly spherical regions the size is roughly the diameter.

[d] The volume is included in the hot intercloud medium.

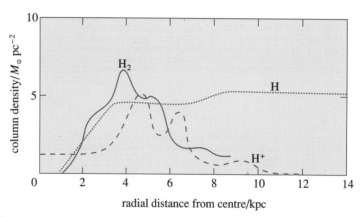

Figure 1.7   Differences in the average distribution of molecular (H_2), atomic (H) and ionized hydrogen (H^+) in the Milky Way.

1.2.5   The rotation and mass of the Milky Way

The fact that much of the disc of the Milky Way rotates with a period of around 2×10^8 years was firmly established in the 1920s by the work of two of Europe's most distinguished 20th century astronomers, Bertil Lindblad (1895–1965) (a Swede) and the Dutchman Jan Hendrik Oort (1900–1992). Their discovery was based on a detailed analysis, by Lindblad, of the movement of the high-velocity stars mentioned earlier. Since the high-velocity stars are not part of the native population of the disc and do not participate in the rotation, they provide a 'reference population' relative to which the Sun's motion can be determined. As a consequence of this work, and other investigations carried out by Oort, the idea emerged that most of the stars in the disc of the Milky Way are in a state of **differential rotation**; in other words, stars that at one instant are 'side by side' at different radial distances from the centre do not remain so as they travel: they have different orbital periods. Figure 1.8 shows how different speeds within the Milky Way lead to differential rotation.

The idea of differential rotation was introduced in Book 1, Subsection 1.2.2.

The idea that speeds can change with distance from the centre in a rotating system is obvious. It is true of points on a wheel, where the rotation is *not* differential – points along a spoke remain 'side by side' and those at large radius have higher speeds than points closer to the centre because they cover a greater distance in the same time. A plot of speed against radial distance for a rotating system is called the **rotation curve** of the system. The rotation curve for a wheel making one revolution per second is shown in Figure 1.9. Figure 1.10 is the rotation curve of planets orbiting the Sun – in this case there *is* differential rotation, a planet closer to the Sun taking less time to complete its orbit than one further out. The way in which speed varies with radial distance is very different in the two cases and is of considerable physical significance.

☐ What parameter can you deduce for a body (such as the Sun) from the time that it takes for another body of much smaller mass (such as a planet), to make a complete orbit under the influence of gravity alone? (This was discussed in Subsection 2.5.1 of Book 1 and in Subsection 1.2.2 of Book 2.)

■ Its mass. (This calculation was the subject of ITQ 1.2 in Book 2.)

The equations used in Books 1 and 2 to deduce the masses of stars and planets were written in terms of the orbital period. When dealing with motions of stars around the Milky Way, it is clearly not possible to measure periods directly, so it is convenient to have the equations in terms of speed v, obtainable from the Doppler effect. For an object in a circular orbit of radius r about a single, much more massive, object (mass M) the appropriate equation is

$$M = rv^2/G \tag{1.1}$$

Rotation curves are plots of v against r, so it is useful to rearrange Equation 1.1 to give

$$v = (GM/r)^{\frac{1}{2}} \tag{1.2}$$

which describes the curve plotted in Figure 1.10.

Obviously, the Milky Way is neither rigid like a wheel, nor does it have a single dominant mass at its centre like the Solar System. Rather, its constituents move under the gravitational influence of all the other constituents. Such a system is generally difficult to analyse, but the situation in the Milky Way is made easier by the fact that most of the matter in the disc appears to be moving in more-or-less circular orbits about the Galactic centre. Furthermore, if the mass is distributed in a spherically symmetrical manner about the centre, then only the

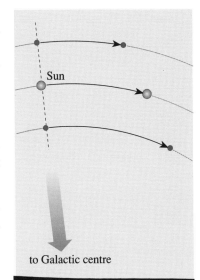

Figure 1.8 The Milky Way is in a state of differential rotation, with material at different radii revolving in the same direction but at different speeds.

This equation is readily obtained from $M = 4\pi^2 r^3/G\tau^2$ (see Book 2, ITQ 1.2) and $v = 2\pi r/\tau$.

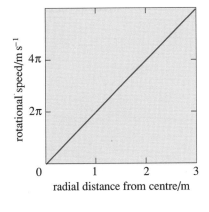

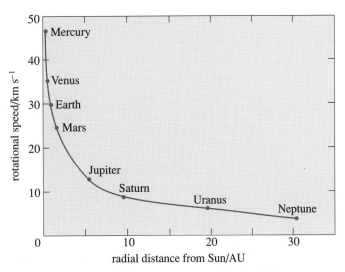

Figure 1.10 The rotation curve of planets of the Solar System.

mass *within* any given orbit affects the motion of an object in that orbit, and even if the distribution is not exactly spherically symmetrical, mass outside the orbit has only a slight effect. If we assume that the Galaxy is fairly symmetrical, then Equation 1.1 gives the mass $M(r)$ enclosed within any radius r from the Galactic centre.

If we want to find the total mass of the Milky Way, we have to study its outskirts, where the orbiting material encloses virtually all the mass of the Galaxy. This is difficult, not least because it is difficult to determine exactly where the Galaxy ends: even if we think there is not much more *visible* matter beyond a certain radius, we cannot be sure that we have found the 'edge' of any dark matter that is associated with the Galaxy. It turns out that plotting a rotation curve, rather than relying on measurements at a single radius, can in principle throw some light on the important question 'Where does the Galaxy end?'. It is possible to use a rotation curve out to some radius to deduce the *distribution* of mass within that radius; that is, to see how $M(r)$ increases with increasing radius. It is then possible both to estimate the total mass within the largest measured radius and to have some idea of whether there is much more mass beyond that.

The usual procedure for deducing $M(r)$ is to take an educated guess at the distribution of matter and then work out theoretically the rotation curve that such a distribution would produce. The initial guess is then adjusted until the theoretical curve agrees with the observed rotation curve.

ITQ 1.2 Use Equation 1.2 to help you to sketch a rotation curve for each of the following distributions of matter: (a) $M(r) = kr$; (b) a uniform sphere, i.e. where $M(r) = k \times$ (volume of sphere enclosed, $\frac{4}{3}\pi r^3$).

Figure 1.11 shows the rotation curve of the Milky Way. Visual observations of stars within the disc are severely limited by the effects of dust – as described in Subsection 1.2.2 – so the curve is compiled from observations of radiation

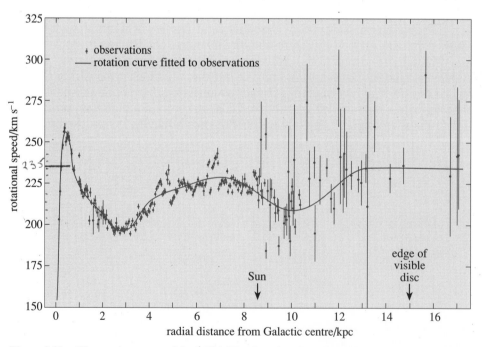

Figure 1.11   The rotation curve of the Milky Way based on Doppler shift studies of H within the Sun's orbit and of CO beyond the Sun's orbit.

emitted by various gases at radio or microwave wavelengths. The Doppler shifts of these lines (hydrogen, H, at 21 cm for example, or carbon monoxide, CO, at 2.6 mm) give information about the orbital motion of the gas. It is clear from Figure 1.11 that there are substantial uncertainties in the measurements, particularly at large radial distances.

Some of the features of Figure 1.11, such as the pronounced peak near the Galactic centre and the sharp dip that follows it, are more likely to be due to the inadequacy of the symmetry assumptions that underpin the analysis rather than real features of the rotation. However, the same is not likely to be true of the flattening of the rotation curve at large distances. This is thought to be a real feature. It is flattening of this kind, extending well beyond the edge of the visible disc, that provides evidence for the presence of a substantial amount of non-luminous matter on the outskirts of the Milky Way – dark matter. If you compare the outer parts of the rotation curve in Figure 1.11 with your answers to ITQ 1.2, you will see that it is similar to the curve for $M(r) = kr$, and does not turn up in the manner corresponding to the uniform sphere (i.e. where $M(r) = k \times \frac{4}{3}\pi r^3$). It is thus clear that the mass does 'thin out' with increasing radius. But if most of the mass of the Galaxy were well within the largest measured radius, the rotation curve would be expected to decline quite rapidly with increasing radial distance, as in Figure 1.10. The answer to the question 'What is the mass of the Galaxy?' really depends on the answer to another: 'Where does the rotation curve turn down?'. Several independent lines of investigation have failed to show any sign of such a decline out to a radius of 20 kpc, indicating a substantial amount of matter at least out to that radius. This matter includes, of course, some form of *dark matter* as discussed at the start of this section.

Despite the large amount of effort invested in studies of rotation curves and the formulation of model mass distributions to explain them, there are still many uncertainties about the true shape of both the rotation curve and the mass distribution of the Milky Way. Different models, according to the assumptions they make about the radius of the Galaxy and the distribution of dark matter, can easily provide estimates of the total Galactic mass that range from a conservative four times the mass of the stars (i.e. $4 \times 10^{11} M_\odot$) to a very substantial 60 times, i.e. $6 \times 10^{12} M_\odot$. There are other methods of assessing the mass of the Galaxy, but they too are based on specific assumptions and do not really help to settle the question. For example, attempts have been made to use the motion of distant halo stars, globular clusters and nearby galaxies as indicators of the Galactic mass. Even the motions of nearby stars have been used, under the assumption that none of them moves fast enough to escape entirely from the gravitational pull of the Milky Way. In an article on the mass of the Galaxy by Michel Fich and Scott Tremaine (*Annual Review of Astronomy and Astrophysics*, 1991, vol. 29, p. 409) the current situation is summarized in the following way:

> What is the mass of the Galaxy? The most important recent progress in addressing this question has been the recognition that it is not well-posed. Several related arguments indicate that there is probably no natural definition of the mass of a giant galaxy like our own...

Table 1.2 summarizes the major structural components of the Milky Way, including some features of those components that will be discussed in the remainder of this chapter.

Table 1.2   The major structural components of the Milky Way

Component	Shape	Dimensions	Dominant constituents [a]		Mass/$M_{\odot}$	Motion
			Stellar	Gaseous [b]		
disc	disc-shaped	diameter $\approx 30\,$kpc thickness $\approx 1\,$kpc	intermediate population I [c] extreme population I in spiral arms	dense and diffuse clouds; warm intercloud medium [d] HII regions and dense clouds concentrated in spiral arms	stars $\sim 10^{11}$ gas $\sim 10^{10}$ dust $\sim 10^{8}$	differential rotation circular orbits around Galactic centre orbits confined to plane of disc matter moves through spiral arms
halo	oblate spheroid [e]	diameter $\approx 40\,$kpc $c/a \approx 0.8$ [e]	extreme population II	corona of tenuous hot gas high-velocity clouds of H	stars $\sim 10^{9}$ gas negligible	elliptical stellar orbits, often highly inclined to Galactic plane
nuclear bulge	oblate spheroid [f]	diameter $\approx 6\,$kpc $c/a \approx 0.7$	intermediate population II extreme population II in inner parts high-metallicity stars close to Galactic centre possible massive black hole at Galactic centre	all forms of hydrogen H_2 dominates in central regions	stars + gas $\sim 10^{10}$	stars move as in rest of halo expanding ring of H_2 close to Galactic centre

[a] This excludes any dark matter.

[b] Dust, which contributes only about 0.1% of the mass of the disc, is concentrated around the mid-plane.

[c] The high-velocity stars within the disc are population II stars passing through the disc.

[d] See Table 1.1.

[e] The term oblate spheroid and the ratio c/a are explained in Subsection 1.4.1.

[f] The shape may be a triaxial ellipsoid (see Chapter 2).

Summary of Section 1.2 and SAQs

1   The Milky Way – our galaxy – consists of three major, directly detectable, structural components; a disc, a surrounding halo and a central nuclear bulge.

2   These three components are thought to be embedded in a massive cloud of dark matter, currently detectable only through its gravitational influence. The nature and distribution of the dark matter are unclear at present, but it is widely thought that its mass might exceed that of the directly detectable matter by a factor of ten.

3   The directly detectable matter consists mainly of stars ($\sim 90\%$ of the Galaxy's mass), gas ($\sim 10\%$) and dust ($\sim 0.1\%$). There are about 10^{11} stars in all, with (very roughly) a total mass of $10^{11}\,M_{\odot}$. The gas is almost entirely 75% hydrogen and 25% helium, by mass, with the hydrogen occurring in the form of molecules, atoms or ions, according to local conditions.

4   Minor, but important, constituents of the Milky Way include cosmic rays, magnetic fields, electromagnetic radiation and neutrinos.

5   The disc of the Milky Way is about 30 kpc in diameter and 1 kpc thick. The nuclear bulge is roughly spherical and has a diameter of about 6 kpc. The halo is also thought to be roughly spherical; its size is difficult to determine but estimates of 40 kpc or so are common.

6   The stars of the Milky Way may be divided into a number of populations, each of which predominates in a particular region of the Galaxy. The youngest stars, those of extreme population I, are found mainly in the spiral arms of the disc. The oldest stars, those of extreme population II, are found mainly in the ancient globular clusters of the halo.

7   The Sun is one of the intermediate population I stars, located in the disc between 7.5 and 10 kpc from the centre of the Galaxy.

8   The disc is in a state of differential rotation, with stars in the vicinity of the Sun taking about 2×10^8 years to make a complete orbit of the Galactic centre. In principle, the rotation curve that describes such circular orbits constrains the total mass of the Galaxy, but in practice the many subtleties and uncertainties involved in the analysis make it impossible to obtain a reliable value.

SAQ 1.1 (Objective 1.2)   Write down a concise description of the distribution of molecular, atomic and ionic hydrogen in the Milky Way. (Ignore the hydrogen contained in stars.)

SAQ 1.2 (Objective 1.3)   Estimate the total mass of helium contained in a ring of interstellar medium that is located between 4.2 and 4.4 kpc from the centre of the Galaxy.

$\frac{\text{helium}}{\text{hydrogen}} : \frac{25}{75} \times 7.8 \times 10^7 M_\odot = 2.6 \times 10^7 M_\odot$

SAQ 1.3 (Objective 1.2)   Why do high-velocity stars have lower metallicity than the Sun?

└ belong to (older) halo population + would ∴ be expected to have lower metallicity than Sun.

SAQ 1.4 (Objective 1.2)   If cosmic rays really originate in supernovae why do we not see them coming directly from the sites of supernovae?

Cosmic rays are charged particles + will be deflected by mag. field in Milky Way.

SAQ 1.5 (Objective 1.4)   The analysis that led to Figure 1.11 assumed that the Sun is located at 8.5 kpc from the Galactic centre . Use this, together with the fact that the Sun is thought to be about 5×10^9 years old, to estimate the number of times the Sun has orbited the Galactic centre.

very approx 21 orbits

1.3   The disc of the Milky Way

The purpose of this section is to provide you with more details about some of the features of the Galactic disc. The section starts with a brief summary of the main features of the disc. The subsections that follow deal with the neighbourhood of the Sun, the spiral arms, and the various clusters and associations of stars that are found within the disc. (Plate 3.5a provides a visual summary of various features of the disc.)

If you have a recording of TV programme 6, now would be a particularly good time to watch it. But if you do not have such a recording, don't worry, since TV programme 6 may be watched at any time during your work on this chapter.

1.3.1 An overview of the disc

As outlined in Section 1.2, the Galactic disc has a diameter of about 30 kpc and a thickness of 1 kpc. It is not actually flat, but warped (tilted) at the edges. This warping is shown in TV programme 6. If it were not for a massive halo, the disc would be more warped.

The disc consists of something like 10^{11} stars, mainly belonging to population I. The population I stars are relatively youthful objects, characterized by intermediate or high metallicities, that move in predominantly circular orbits around the Galactic centre. The density of stars falls off rapidly with distance from the Galactic centre and with distance from the mid-plane of the disc. In recent years there has been much debate about whether or not there is a **thick disc** (a few kpc thick) in addition to the familiar thin disc. Though it is widely thought that there is such a component and that its properties are intermediate between those of the (normal) thin disc and those of the halo, the thick disc will be ignored in the rest of this discussion.

About 10% (perhaps as much as 30%) of the mass of the disc is in the interstellar medium, mainly hydrogen, but with the usual mixture (25% by mass) of helium. About 50% of the hydrogen is contained in thousands of cool, dense clouds (Plate 1.21) each of which is typically several parsecs across. The dense clouds are found throughout the disc but they are particularly numerous in a ring between about 4 and 7 kpc from the centre of the Milky Way. In the dense clouds the hydrogen is present in molecular form. Some diffuse clouds also contain hydrogen that is mainly in molecular form. The rest of the hydrogen exists mainly in the form of neutral atoms, and forms part of the warm intercloud medium that occupies 30% of the volume of the disc. The intercloud medium may itself be loosely regarded as a disc about 300 pc thick that is more-or-less uniformly distributed across the Galactic disc. The relatively small amount of ionized hydrogen present is partly contained in the hot and warm intercloud media and partly, but much more spectacularly, in regions of glowing gas (Plate 1.16) that are frequently found in association with the dense clouds. These regions of glowing ionized hydrogen, known as HII regions, and other components of the interstellar medium are described more fully in Book 1, Subsection 5.3.2.

☐ Why are hot HII regions often found in association with cool dense clouds?

■ New stars form within cool dense clouds (Book 1, Section 3.2). New-born stars (particularly the short-lived but highly luminous main sequence stars of spectral classes O and B) photoionize hydrogen in their vicinity and thus produce HII regions in close association with dense clouds.

One of the best ways of making sense of the disc is to remember that it is the main focus for star formation in the Milky Way. By thinking of the disc as 'a machine for making stars', it is possible to tie together the presence of young high-metallicity stars, dense molecular clouds and HII regions. It is also possible, using this idea, to rationalize the existence of spiral arms and to explain why the disc contains thousands of open star clusters and other physical associations of young stars.

If dark matter really does exist, then it is quite possible – some would say almost certain – that there is a good deal of it within the disc. However, stars and gas are so dense in the disc that it is possible that visible matter dominates there. Studies of the motion of stars perpendicular to the disc indicate that no more than 30–50% of the disc's matter is dark. This should be contrasted with the situation in the Galaxy as a whole, where 90% of the matter may be dark, perhaps even more.

1.3.2 The neighbourhood of the Sun

The region of the disc neighbouring the Sun obviously holds a certain parochial fascination for us, but it also has a number of less anthropocentric features that make it especially intriguing.

One of the most striking consequences of the Sun's astronomical setting is the clear concentration of surrounding material in a plane. This is shown, at several different wavelengths, in Plate 3.4. As you know, this is due to the fact that the Sun is located near the mid-plane of the Milky Way's disc, a good way in from the edge. The **Galactic plane** is very nearly the same as the mid-plane, differing only in that, whereas the intersection of the mid-plane with the celestial sphere does not *quite* form a great circle in our skies (*Project file*, Subsection 1.2.3), the intersection of the Galactic plane with the celestial sphere *does* form a great circle. The proximity of the mid-plane to the Galactic plane is emphasized in Plate 3.4 by presenting each of the all-sky views in **Galactic coordinates** and using a projection that has the Galactic plane running horizontally across the middle. The centre of each image lies in the direction of the constellation Sagittarius, since that is known to be the direction of the Galactic centre. (Just how this came to be known will be discussed in Subsection 1.4.1.

A note on Galactic coordinates

The Galactic system of coordinates uses the Galactic plane and the direction of the Galactic centre as its frame of reference. The direction of any object in our sky can be expressed in terms of its **Galactic latitude** (b) and **Galactic longitude** (l) which, like geographical latitude and longitude, are angles expressed in degrees. Figure 1.12 shows how Galactic latitude and longitude are defined. Galactic longitude ranges from $l = 0°$ (towards the Galactic centre) to $l = 360°$, and latitude from $b = +90°$ to $b = -90°$. The **Galactic equator** is defined by those points which have $b = 0°$, and, because the Sun lies close to the mid-plane of the Galaxy, objects in the disc lie close to the Galactic equator. In terms of conventional celestial coordinates (*Project file*) the Galactic centre is located at right ascension $\alpha = 17$ h 45.7 min and declination $\delta = -29° \, 0'$; the Galactic coordinates of this point are, by definition, longitude $l = 0° \, 0'$ and latitude $b = 0° \, 0'$. Note that Galactic coordinates are (like celestial coordinates) *Earth*-centred. They are *not* centred on the Galactic centre.

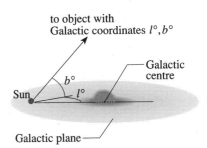

Figure 1.12   Galactic coordinates are centred on the Sun, and use the Galactic plane and the Galactic centre to define a frame of reference. A positive latitude is shown.

The advantage of using Galactic coordinates to display images such as Plate 3.4 is that the Galactic plane runs across the picture and so the directions of other objects relative to the plane are easy to see.

☐   Plate 3.3 is a wide-angle view, in visible light, directed towards the centre of the Milky Way. Why are you unable to see the Galactic centre itself in this photograph?

■   Material in the plane of the Galaxy, mainly dust, scatters light and prevents direct visual examination of the Galactic centre (Subsection 1.2.2).

In the disc of the Milky Way, obscuring material makes it impossible to see stars of solar luminosity, or less, if they are more than about 1 kpc away, and even the brightest disc objects are unobservable, at optical wavelengths, beyond about 5 kpc. Nonetheless, the region that can be surveyed visually is large enough to provide some evidence of the overall spiral structure of the Milky Way. In particular, as Figure 1.13 indicates, the local distribution of bright HII regions and prominent clusters of young stars seems to trace out several parallel strips that can be interpreted as neighbouring spiral arms. The Sun itself seems to be contained within such a strip of astronomically young objects, called the **Orion arm**. It is unclear whether this is really a spiral arm in its own right or simply a 'side spur' belonging to some other arm.

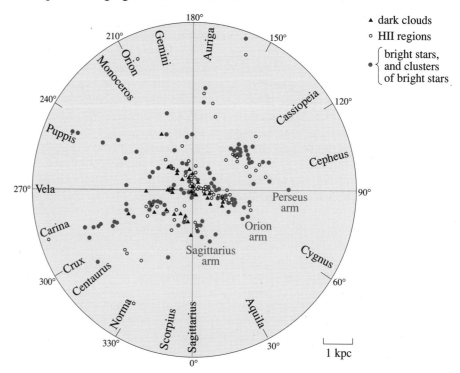

Figure 1.13 The distribution of dark clouds, bright HII regions and prominent clusters of young stars in the solar neighbourhood. The location of the Sun is at the centre. This is a *plan* view of the Galactic disc, with galactic longitude shown. This plan view should be compared with Figure 1.1.

A plot, in Galactic coordinates, of some of the nearby star clusters that encircle the Sun reveals another interesting feature. These star clusters form a band or belt – known as **Gould's belt** – that is inclined relative to the Galactic plane (Figure 1.14). The reason for this inclination is not clear, but it is usually taken as evidence that the clusters making up Gould's belt were formed by some common, large-scale process. What this process might have been will be considered in the next subsection.

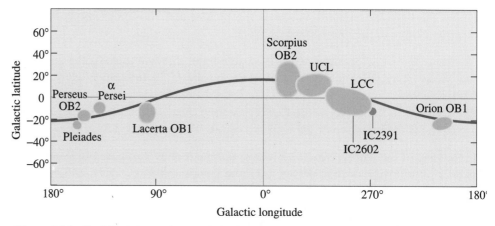

Figure 1.14 Gould's belt – a band of clusters and associations of bright young stars (OB associations) that encircles the Sun. Note that Gould's belt is inclined relative to the Galactic plane, which is represented by the horizontal line running across the middle of this figure.

ITQ 1.3   What is the inclination of Gould's belt relative to the Galactic plane? *Inclined at about 20° to the Galactic plane.*

Another peculiarity of our part of the disc is that stars of all kinds seem to be more densely packed in our immediate neighbourhood than they are in surrounding regions. Counts of star numbers in different directions indicate that their (number) density at a distance of 500–1 000 pc is only about half the local value. Of course, great care is needed in carrying out such counts. For one thing the majority of the stars are intrinsically faint and correspondingly difficult to detect. Furthermore, the obscuring effect of dust is very severe in the disc and must be properly taken into account. Nonetheless, it seems that the Sun really does occupy a region of enhanced star density, known as the **Local System**. Whether or not the existence of the Local System is related to the presence of Gould's belt is unclear. It is tempting to make such an association and to claim that both are a result of our being within a spiral arm. However, as mentioned earlier, spiral arms are generally thought to stand out because of their light output, whereas the Local System represents an enhancement in the *mass* of stars in the solar neighbourhood.

A final topic that deserves inclusion in this survey of the Sun's neighbourhood is the state of the local interstellar medium. It almost goes without saying that the local ISM is expected to be about 75% hydrogen and 25% helium (by mass); the real question is what form does the hydrogen take? Are we in a dense cloud, an HII region or some other well-defined feature, or are we simply bathed in warm intercloud medium like so much else of the disc? This question is actually rather difficult to answer because of the difficulty of measuring localized rather than averaged properties of the ISM along a particular direction of observation. However, the fact that X-rays can be seen coming from all directions indicates that we are not enclosed by a substantial cloud of molecular or atomic hydrogen. Rather, we seem to be contained within a bubble of hot gas, perhaps created by a supernova that occurred about 10^5 years ago. Studies of absorption features in the UV spectra of stars at various known distances indicate that this so-called **Local Bubble** is about 200 pc across and that it contains a number of warm clouds that may have cold centres. The Sun seems to be located on the edge of one of these warm clouds, though when we look through it – in the direction of the constellation Sagittarius – it seems to cause little absorption, so it cannot be rich in dust. A highly schematic diagram of the Local Bubble is shown in Figure 1.15. (Another view of the Local Bubble is provided in Plate 1.13.)

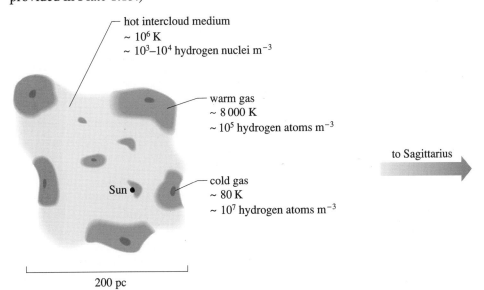

hot intercloud medium
~ 10^6 K
~ 10^3–10^4 hydrogen nuclei m^{-3}

warm gas
~ 8 000 K
~ 10^5 hydrogen atoms m^{-3}

to Sagittarius

Sun •

cold gas
~ 80 K
~ 10^7 hydrogen atoms m^{-3}

200 pc

Figure 1.15   A highly schematic representation of the Local Bubble of the ISM that contains the Sun.

1.3.3 The spiral arms – their nature, origin and influence

It is clear from the general overview of the Milky Way, and from the discussion of the Sun's neighbourhood, that spiral arms are thought to be important features of the disc, though really firm evidence of the spiral structure is hard to obtain. Nonetheless, it *is* believed that we live in a spiral galaxy and various attempts have been made to determine the number and location of the arms. The result of one attempt at mapping the positions of HII regions, thought to be especially correlated with spiral arms, is shown in Figure 1.16. Other evidence for spiral arms comes from observations of clouds of atomic hydrogen, and of dense clouds, also thought to be correlated with spiral arms. When looking at 'artists' conceptions' of the Milky Way that include beautifully unbroken spiral arms, it should be remembered that scientific backing for such detailed views is almost entirely lacking. Remember, too, that there may be a central bar in the Milky Way, rarely shown in such 'artistic' pictures.

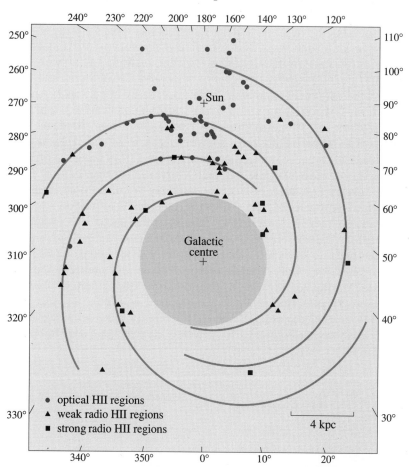

Figure 1.16   The spiral arms of the Galaxy? An attempt at mapping the spiral arms based on optical HII regions, strong radio HII regions and weak radio HII regions. Galactic longitudes are shown.

As indicated earlier, it is widely believed that spiral arms are concentrations of bright stars rather than mass. They stand out because they contain bright HII regions and luminous O and B class stars. Objects of this kind are associated with star-forming regions. O and B stars are so short-lived that, if you see them, they cannot be far from where they were born so it is usual to regard the spiral arms as the main locales of star formation in the Milky Way. What is much harder to explain is *why* star formation should occur along reasonably well-defined spiral tracks. It's all very well that star-forming regions light up the spiral arms like a set of flash bulbs, but what actually causes them? And how do the arms manage to persist over long periods of time, as their presence in a high proportion of external galaxies implies?

In trying to account for the existence and persistence of spiral arms one point must be kept clearly in mind: if the arms were composed of an *unchanging* population of stars, the differential rotation of the disc would cause the shape of the arms to alter with time and an initially 'realistic' pattern of arms would soon cease to resemble any observed spiral arms. This latter problem is called the **winding dilemma** and deserves some extra consideration.

ITQ 1.4   Imagine, somewhat unrealistically, that the rotation curve of the Milky Way (Figure 1.11) can be represented by a constant rotation speed of 220 km s^{-1} for all radial distances from 4–10 kpc from the Galactic centre, and suppose that a pattern of spiral arms like that shown in Figure 1.16 already existed in the Galaxy 5×10^9 years ago, when the Sun formed.

(a) How many orbits of the Galactic centre would the inner end of one of the arms, located 4 kpc from the Galactic centre, have completed since the formation of the Sun?   ~ 45 orbits

(b) How many orbits would the outer end of one of the arms, located 10 kpc from the Galactic centre, have completed in the same time?   ~ 18 orbits

(c) If the spiral arms had been made of the same population of stars throughout the lifetime of the Sun, what would they look like now? How well does your answer correspond to the actual appearance of spiral arms?

Even allowing for the oversimplifications of ITQ 1.4 it is fairly clear that, although spiral arms may represent a persistent *pattern*, they cannot always be made of the same population of differentially rotating stars if they are as persistent as we think they are. So, how are the spiral arms explained? There is general agreement amongst astronomers that there is a pattern of density enhancements which leads to the formation of bright stars, but there is less consensus on how such enhancements might be produced and maintained. The mechanism described below is favoured by many, but by no means all, astronomers. Since it was first proposed, several other possible mechanisms have been suggested.

The conventional explanation of spiral arms is based on the **density wave theory** developed by the American astronomers C. C. Lin and Frank H. Shu in the 1960s. In their work the idea that the disc is a smooth, axially symmetric distribution of matter in a state of steady differential rotation is regarded as no more than a first approximation to the truth. A more realistic picture is adopted in which it is accepted that there will be departures from this overly-simple, highly symmetric view. In the Lin–Shu approach it is assumed that the disc will contain regions in which the density is enhanced relative to the surrounding material. These enhancements will not be particularly strong: the total density in the enhanced regions will only be a few per cent greater than the average density, but even this is highly significant. Now, generally speaking, density enhancements in the disc will, according to their size, either disrupt the disc completely or soon be smeared out by differential rotation. However, in a highly mathematical treatment, Lin and Shu tried to show that there were certain patterns of density enhancement that could effectively feed off themselves and become self-perpetuating. One of these long-lived self-consistent patterns of density enhancement is shown schematically in Figure 1.17; such patterns are known as **spiral density waves**.

Interestingly, the density wave maintains its shape as it rotates (it is often said to rotate *rigidly*, as its rotation resembles that of a wheel), despite the fact that the disc material from which it is made rotates *differentially*. In fact, the

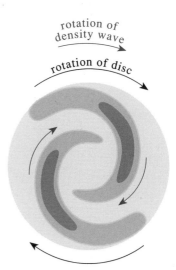

Figure 1.17   A spiral density wave. This pattern of enhanced density (as shown by the intensity of shading) rotates in the same sense as the orbiting disc material but at a generally slower rate. Only towards the outer edge of the disc, at the so-called co-rotation radius, does the rotation speed of the density wave equal that of the matter in the disc.

density wave moves more slowly than the matter in the disc. Only towards the outer edge of the pattern, where the matter in the disc rotates slowly, does the rotation speed of the disc equal that of the density wave. The radius at which this occurs is called the **co-rotation radius**. Thus, throughout most of the disc, stars and gas will approach the slowly moving density wave from behind, pass through it, experiencing compression in the process, and then move on ahead of the wave's leading edge. In this sense, the matter moves through the density wave rather than the density wave moving through the matter.

ITQ 1.5 Assuming that the co-rotation radius of the Milky Way is at 15 kpc from the Galactic centre, and using the theoretical rotation curve given in Figure 1.11, draw the rotation curve of a spiral density wave and estimate the speed at which the Sun would approach such a wave. $(220 - 133)$ kms^{-1} = 87 kms^{-1}

There is some disagreement about the mechanism that may produce and maintain a density wave – the mechanism described below is just one of several possibilities for maintaining the wave.

The basic density wave pattern is shown in Figure 1.18 where the thin black lines show the circular orbits that would be followed in the absence of density waves and the thick blue lines show the location of the density waves themselves. Remember, the waves are density enhancements, so material at points A, B and C will actually experience a gravitational pull due to each wave. What will be the effect of these additional gravitational forces? In the case of material at point B the answer is simple; the arms are equidistant from B so there will be roughly equal inward and outward pulls, these will cancel and the material will continue to follow the circular orbit. For the material at C the outcome is quite different. The outward pull will be greater than the inward pull, and this will distort the orbit in such a way that the material spends longer in the vicinity of the density wave than it would have done if it had remained on its original circular orbit. Similar comments apply to material at point A. Consequently material is slowed as it passes through the density wave and is thus able to contribute to the enhanced mass of material that comprises the wave. A useful analogy to keep in mind is that of traffic tailing back from a slowly moving lorry on a narrow road. The vehicles in the tailback move slowly and are constantly changing as some overtake the lorry and others join the rear of the tailback, but the tailback always persists.

So much for persistent density waves, but what do they have to do with spiral arms? Although the density waves are density enhancements of stars and gas, the gas within a wave has a density that is enhanced far more than might be expected on the basis of the modest overall density increase. It is thought that a dense cloud entering a density wave from the rear would encounter a rapid increase in ambient density, as indicated in Figure 1.19. For a giant molecular cloud complex, just on the verge of forming stars, the encounter with the sudden increase in density (even only a few per cent) might well be enough to trigger star formation within it. It is this feature of the density wave – its ability to trigger star formation and thus give rise to coherent patterns of star formation – that is thought to account for the presence of bright young stars that light up the arm. Material probably takes about 3×10^7 years to pass through the densest part of an arm, as indicated in Figure 1.19. This is long enough for a star-forming cloud to produce some bright O and B class stars (together with the associated HII regions) and for some of those highly luminous stars to live out their entire main sequence life.

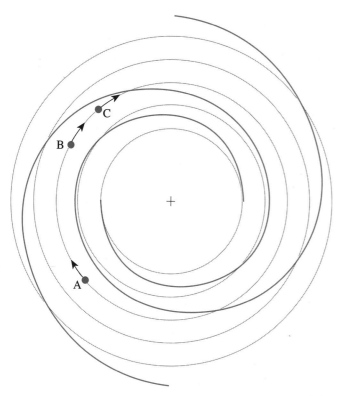

Figure 1.18 Persistence of spiral density waves. Material particles, at points A, B and C, following roughly circular orbits (thin black lines) in the direction indicated, pass through the spiral density waves (thick blue lines), hesitating in their vicinity.

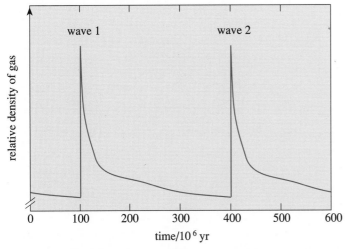

Figure 1.19 Average relative gas density encountered during an orbit of the Milky Way. (Highly schematic.)

Density wave theory is popular with many astronomers because it is reasonably well-defined and makes precise predictions. However, given the present state of the observational evidence it could hardly be said to be well confirmed. Moreover, there are still some unresolved issues within the theory, some technical, others quite basic such as the origin of the density enhancements. (This latter point is usually explained by saying that the waves are stirred up by some kind of external influence such as another galaxy, or perhaps some sort of asymmetry near the Galactic centre.) In the absence of clear confirmation of the Lin–Shu theory, other explanations of spiral arms have been developed. Many of these alternative explanations are modifications or extensions of the basic density wave theory, but at least one other idea has captured a good deal of attention – **sequential star formation** (also known as **self-sustaining star formation**). The basis of this idea is simply that a star-forming region may produce such an outburst of energy that it can heat the surrounding gas enough to produce shock-waves that lead to an increased density and trigger star formation in a neighbouring region. (If newly-formed stars cannot do this on their own, then the supernovae that some of them eventually produce probably can.) If sequential star formation of this kind can occur, and it is believed that it does, then differential rotation might be able to smear the star-forming regions into spiral arms. Computer models have given some support to this idea, but the general attitude is still one of caution. Sequential star formation may well have played a role in the development of the Milky Way – but density waves are still a widely-preferred explanation of the grand design of spiral arms.

Now that you have finished this subsection you should view video sequence 9 which may help you to visualize more fully the rather complicated motions involved in the spiral arms.

1.3.4 Open clusters and OB associations

Because of their tendency to cluster along the band of the Milky Way, open clusters used to be called *galactic clusters*. Though this term is still seen from time to time it is now regarded as potentially confusing (galaxy clusters, for instance, are quite different) and its use is strongly disfavoured.

Open clusters are another prominent feature of the Galactic disc. Such clusters are localized regions where the (number) density of stars is enhanced relative to that of the immediately surrounding area. A typical open cluster would be 2–3 pc across and might include anything from a few tens of stars to many hundreds.

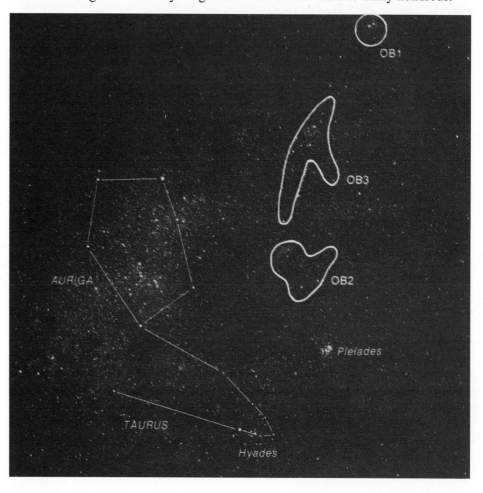

Figure 1.20 Open clusters and OB associations in Auriga and Taurus.

These figures are very crude, but even the richest open clusters would have a fairly loose structure and would contain no more than a few thousand stars. Some open clusters are sufficiently prominent to be visible to the naked eye, notably the Pleiades (Plate 1.22b) in the constellation of Taurus, Praesepe in Cancer, the Hyades in Taurus (Figure 1.20) and the famous double cluster, h and χ Persei, in Perseus. In all, something like 200 open clusters are now known, though it is fairly certain that this is only a fraction (perhaps about 1%) of the full number to be found in the disc.

Not only are open clusters found in the disc, they are particularly common in the spiral arms. Indeed, since they are composed of population I stars and usually include an above-average number of bright stars, they are amongst the objects used to trace the location of the spiral arms. The concentration of open clusters in the spiral arms must mean that the clusters have relatively short lives, otherwise differential rotation relative to the arms would carry them out of the arms and spread them across the disc. This deduction is confirmed by detailed studies of the stars contained in individual clusters. It is quite clear from such studies that the stars in each cluster were formed together at essentially the same time and that the cluster as a whole (with very few exceptions) is unlikely to survive for more than 10^9 years. The smallest clusters live for even shorter periods, just a few million years, which explains the strong correlation with spiral arms.

ITQ 1.6 Why would a cluster lifetime of 10^9 years be inconsistent with the correlation between open clusters and spiral arms?

Although open clusters are not particularly dense aggregates of stars, it is thought that each one is bound together by the mutual gravitational attraction of its members. If so, why do the clusters have a lifetime that is much shorter than that of many of the stars they contain? What disrupts the clusters and causes them to dissipate? Many possible answers suggest themselves, since a cluster moving in the disc must face many hazards. The cluster might be torn apart by a gravitational encounter with some other object such as a giant molecular cloud complex or another cluster. Even if it avoids this fate, gravitational interactions between the members of a cluster can sometimes give one star so much more energy than its partners that it entirely escapes from the cluster. Given long enough, this process, usually referred to as *evaporation*, would eventually disperse all the clusters. A third process that disrupts clusters is differential rotation. The stars in an open cluster are orbiting the Galactic centre even while they are moving around one another. Working out the consequences of this kind of combined motion is not easy, but it appears that open clusters are stretched, distorted and eventually destroyed by differential rotation (which is itself a consequence of the combined gravitational pull of the Galaxy's constituents).

Stellar aggregates of another kind may also be found in the disc, particularly within the spiral arms. These are the **OB associations** (Book 1, Subsection 5.3.2), first noted in 1949 by the Armenian astrophysicist V. A. Ambartsumian (1908–). OB associations have diameters of 100 pc or so and densities not much greater than their general surroundings. However, they are distinguished by the fact that they contain an unusually high proportion of O and B class stars (Figure 1.20). In addition, many OB associations have a very young open cluster at their centre. The presence of numerous O and B class stars, which have a very short main sequence lifetime, together with young open clusters is a sure sign that the OB associations are themselves young objects, dating back no more than a few million years. About 70 OB associations are known, including the very nearby ones that make up Gould's belt (Figure 1.14). Once again, they have been used to trace out the spiral arms, just like the open clusters.

1   The Galactic disc contains young stars and is the main focus of continuing star formation. It also contains older stars.

2   The disc is about 30 kpc in diameter and 1 kpc thick. Its directly detectable constituents are mostly stars, gas and dust. The density of stars falls off with distance from the centre and with distance from the mid-plane. The gas is more strongly concentrated around the mid-plane than are the stars.

3   The disc is thought to be threaded by bright spiral arms, though it is difficult to determine their exact configuration. There may also be a central bar.

4   The spiral arms are sites of active star formation. Attempts to trace the arms make use of young, short-lived features of the disc such as bright HII regions, young open clusters and OB associations. Dense clouds and clouds of neutral hydrogen are also used as tracers.

5   It is thought that the large-scale patterns of star formation that highlight the spiral arms might be caused by density waves – relatively slow-moving patterns of density enhancement that rotate as if rigidly around the Galactic centre. Differentially rotating disc material, particularly giant molecular cloud complexes, entering such regions of enhanced density would undergo collisions with the gas already there. Such collisions may trigger the birth of stars which, given the size of the giant clouds, would be expected to form in clusters.

SAQ 1.6 (Objective 1.6)   Assuming that optical views of the disc of the Milky Way are limited to a range of 5 kpc, estimate the fraction of the disc's volume that can be surveyed optically. What is the main cause of this limitation?

SAQ 1.7 (Objective 1.6)   If the Sun was born in association with other stars, and originally formed part of an open cluster (which is far from certain), why can we no longer see any evidence of that cluster?

SAQ 1.8 (Objective 1.7)   How does density wave theory solve the winding dilemma?

SAQ 1.9 (Objective 1.7)   Make a list of the kinds of astronomical objects that can be used in attempts to trace the spiral arms of the Milky Way.

SAQ 1.10 (Objective 1.6)   If you were to draw an all-sky map showing the location of all the known open clusters, what would you expect it to look like? There is no need actually to draw such a map, but you should assume that it uses Galactic coordinates and involves the kind of projection that has the Galactic plane running horizontally across the middle of the map (as in Figure 1.14).

1.4   The halo of the Milky Way

This section deals with the largest of the structural components – the halo. As in the last section, it opens with a brief overview, partly to remind you of what was said in Section 1.2 and partly to provide you with some insight into what is to come later. The subsections that follow provide more details about globular clusters and the gaseous content of the halo.

1.4.1 An overview of the halo

In contrast to the disc, which constantly recycles its material and renews itself through the process of star formation, the halo is a very old and relatively inactive part of the Milky Way. It consists mainly of old or very old population II stars that are poorly endowed with heavy elements and which move in roughly elliptical orbits that are often highly inclined to the Galactic plane. Stars following such orbits will plunge through the disc from time to time, but the spaces between stars, even in the disc, are so great that collisions are highly improbable. Nonetheless, stellar orbits that pass through the disc are subject to gravitational distortion and are unlikely to be 'closed' curves in the same way that planetary orbits are (almost) closed.

☐ Which spectral classes of main sequence star would you expect to be common in the halo? What other kinds of star are likely to be abundant there?

■ Only long-lived main sequence stars should be common; those of spectral classes K and M, for example. Apart from old main sequence stars there should be other, more highly evolved, stars such as those that are burning hydrogen in a shell around their cores, and red giants that are burning helium in their cores. Even more highly evolved objects, such as white dwarfs, might also be expected.

These expectations are borne out. There is evidence for some 'young' blueish–white stars in the halo but they are certainly rare and may well have escaped from the disc since the low density of gas in the halo makes it an unlikely site for star formation. Such stars would have been liberated by gravitational encounters with other stars or as a consequence of supernova explosions.

The total mass of the halo stars is about $10^9 \, M_\odot$, roughly 1% of the mass of the disc. The halo stars are more densely concentrated towards the middle of the Milky Way, but very close to the centre – within 1 kpc or so – they are so greatly outnumbered by stars belonging to the disc and bulge, and so severely obscured, that they cannot be distinguished as a separate population.

As explained in Section 1.2, the shape and size of the halo are poorly determined. Until recently it was usual to see the halo described as spherical and it can still be thought of in roughly those terms. However, recent measurements have indicated that it is flatter than previously thought. Shape determinations are based on counts of the number of halo stars in a plane surrounding the Sun that is at right angles to the plane of the Galaxy and perpendicular to the direction of the Galactic centre (see Figure 1.21). Stars in this particular plane, at a given distance

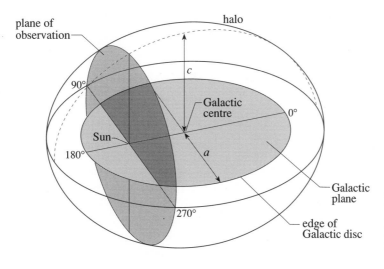

Figure 1.21 Assessing the shape of the halo. Stars are counted in the plane of observation over a range of Galactic latitudes in order to determine the axis ratio *c/a* of the halo.

from the Sun, will all be at a common distance from the Galactic centre, thus counts of such stars can be used to assess the shape of a section through the halo (also shown in Figure 1.21). Current values for the ratio of the axes a and c shown in Figure 1.21 indicate that $c/a \approx 0.8$, making the halo a flattened (oblate) **spheroid** rather than a sphere.

About 1% of the halo stars are contained in globular clusters. These are relatively prominent objects that can be easily picked out and studied. Over a hundred globular clusters are known to be associated with the Milky Way, and once the effects of obscuration are taken into account it seems likely that the total number present is between 150 and 200. The properties of individual globular clusters will be discussed in the next subsection, but it is appropriate to say something about their overall distribution here, since it may help to determine the size of the halo.

Globular clusters are more numerous close to the Galactic centre. This is shown quite clearly in Figure 1.22 and was first recognized by the American astronomer Harlow Shapley (1885–1972). In 1917, on the basis of his studies of globular clusters, Shapley asserted that the centre of the Milky Way was in the direction of the constellation of Sagittarius, at a distance of about 20 kpc. This figure, we now know, is too high, though the basic idea and the direction are correct. Shapley overestimated the distance to the Galactic centre because he underestimated the extent to which interstellar matter dimmed the light from the globular clusters.

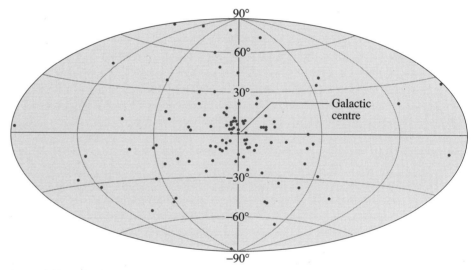

Figure 1.22 The distribution of globular clusters in the sky. This all-sky map has been plotted using Galactic coordinates and a projection that has the mid-plane of the Galaxy running horizontally across the map. Note that the globular clusters are gathered around the centre of the Milky Way.

☐ What is the present estimate of the distance to the Galactic centre?

■ About 8.5 kpc ($\approx 28\,000$ light years).

Using modern (and, we hope, accurate) estimates of globular cluster distances reveals an interesting fact. Although there are many globular clusters within 20 kpc of the disc of the Galaxy, and a few beyond 37 kpc, there are none at all in between. It may be that the outlying ones indicate just how extensive the halo is, but some authors take the view that these are more like 'satellites' of the Milky Way and treat the break at 20 kpc as a rough indication of the outer edge of the halo. More detailed studies indicate another interesting fact: some of the globular clusters that lie close to the disc of the Galaxy are significantly richer in heavy elements than those found further away. This has led to the recognition that about

30% of the known globular clusters should really be classified as **disc globulars** and should be clearly distinguished from the lower-metallicity globulars that are found throughout the halo.

1.4.2 Globular clusters: their nature and significance

Globular clusters are spectacularly beautiful – colour pictures of several are included in Plate 3.6. As noted in Section 1.2, they are up to about 50 pc in diameter and contain 10^5–10^6 stars. As their name implies, they have a spherical shape and, like the halo itself, they are more densely concentrated towards their centres. Because of the central concentration their middles are often overexposed in photographs, so it looks as if they have a solid lump at their core. However, this is not really the case, as can be seen from Plate 3.6e, which provides a short exposure of the core of one particular globular cluster. A typical value for the number density of stars at the centre of the globular cluster is perhaps $10^5 \, pc^{-3}$. This is very much higher than the number density of stars in the solar neighbourhood ($\sim 0.1 \, pc^{-3}$) but it still leaves plenty of space between individual stars.

It has been known since the early days of X-ray astronomy that some globular clusters are sources of X-rays. This fact may be connected with the high central density of globular clusters. It is inevitable that in the dense cluster cores, encounters between stars will be relatively common. This might lead to the formation of a massive black hole that could be the source of the X-rays, though there is no evidence for this. On the whole it seems more likely that many close binary systems develop there, and that it is the exchange of mass from one component of the binary to the other that is the cause of the X-rays (see Plate 1.25). In order for mass to be exchanged, one of the stars in such a system has probably evolved to the stage where it is distended and fills its Roche lobe (Book 1, Section 4.5), or is expelling matter in a powerful stellar wind. For the mass exchange to lead to X-ray emission, the other component of the binary has probably evolved into a white dwarf or possibly a neutron star. Matter falling onto such a compact star can, under the right circumstances, produce X-rays, as explained in Book 1.

Recent (March 1994) images from the repaired Hubble Space Telescope reveal no evidence for any black holes.

Globular clusters have played a significant part in the history of astronomy through their role in locating the centre of the Milky Way. They continue to be of importance for a number of reasons, particularly because of their great age and the relative ease with which this can be determined. The globular clusters are the oldest known systems of stars. They are thought to have formed at an early stage during the evolution of the Milky Way, possibly even before the Galaxy itself was a well defined entity. In view of their ancient origin, they may be able to teach us a good deal about the formation of the Milky Way. In addition, the oldest globular clusters provide a lower limit on the age of the Universe. Obviously the Universe must be older than the oldest globular clusters it contains, but there have been times when observationally determined cluster ages have exceeded some theoretical predictions of the age of the Universe. Such conflicts have been a source of great controversy.

Figure 1.23 is a schematic representation of the Hertzsprung–Russell (H–R) diagram of a globular cluster. It shows the temperature and luminosity of each of the stars in the cluster, or at least a representative sample of them. The age of any individual globular cluster is determined by compiling and analysing its own individual H–R diagram. The principles underlying this analysis are fairly straightforward and can be understood on the basis of what you learned about H–R diagrams in Chapters 2 and 3 of Book 1. It is presumed that the stars comprising the cluster were all formed at approximately the same time and had the same initial composition. So, when it was still young, all the cluster's stars would have belonged to the main sequence and the cluster's H–R diagram would

Because of observational difficulties, the H–R diagrams of real globular clusters are often much less complete than the idealized example of Figure 1.23.

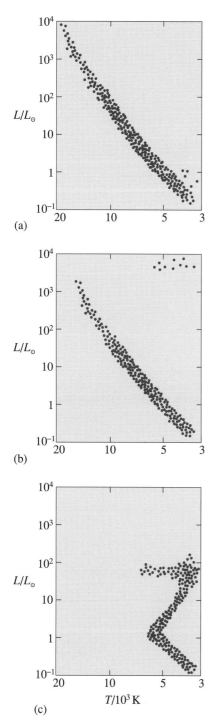

have looked something like Figure 1.24a. As the cluster aged, the more massive stars of high luminosity would have soon left the main sequence and evolved to become supergiants. The point on the cluster's H–R diagram corresponding to stars that are just reaching the end of their time on the main sequence is called the **main sequence turn-off point**. With the further passage of time more and more stars would have evolved into supergiants or red giants (according to mass) and the main sequence would have become progressively depopulated. The H–R diagram of the middle-aged cluster would have looked something like Figure 1.24b. Eventually, as the cluster continued to evolve, its H–R diagram would have acquired the form of Figure 1.24c – which resembles Figure 1.23. The age of an individual globular cluster can be gauged by making a theoretical estimate of the time required for the H–R diagram to evolve into the observed form.

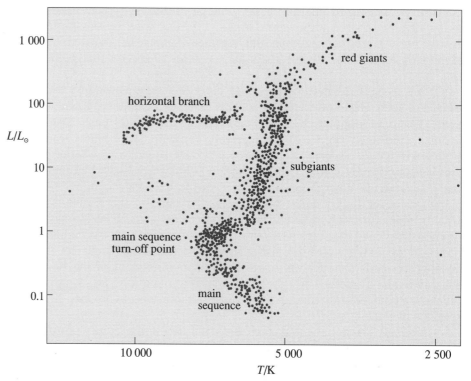

Figure 1.23   A schematic representation of the H–R diagram of a globular cluster. Some of the major features of such a diagram have been named. The physical significance of these regions is the subject of ITQ 1.7. (The main sequence in Figure 1.23 is lower than in Book 1, because the stars in ancient globular clusters are of very low metallicity.)

ITQ 1.7   Figure 1.23 labels the main sequence, the main sequence turn-off point, subgiants and red giants. On the basis of what you learnt in Block 1, together with comments made earlier in this chapter, explain the physical significance of these designated regions by describing, in general terms, the main energy-generating processes taking place inside the stars that occupy them.

The process of making a theoretical estimate of the time required for a cluster's H–R diagram to acquire a specific form is not an easy one. It usually involves the use of large and sophisticated computer programs to model the evolution of a set of stars thought to be broadly representative of the cluster (or at least of those parts of it that contributed to the observed H–R diagram). The theoretical stellar models embodied in these programs are, despite their complexity, much simpler than real stars so great care must be exercised to make them as realistic as possible. Not the least of the problems is that the details of stellar evolution are sensitive to the (initial) proportion of heavy elements in a star, so this must be

Figure 1.24   The evolution of the H–R diagram of a cluster of stars.
(a) When the cluster is less than a few million years old, essentially all the stars belong to the main sequence.
(b) After a few million years all of the high-mass stars will have left the main sequence. Less massive stars will still be members of the main sequence.
(c) After many billions of years only a rump of low-mass main sequence stars will remain. The surviving inter-mediate-mass stars will have evolved into red giants, or will be in the process of doing so.

estimated on the basis of current observations of stellar atmospheres or of clouds. Also, some aspects of stellar modelling are particularly difficult, notably the treatment of convection zones (see Book 1, Section 1.5). Despite these difficulties, a good deal of effort has gone into the computation of theoretical cluster H–R diagrams that can be compared with observational data. The most age-sensitive feature of these diagrams is usually the location of the main sequence turn-off point, so it is this that is actually used to date the clusters. Figure 1.25 shows a comparison between the predicted forms of the turn-off and the observations for one particular cluster. As you can see, the age indicated in this case is about 15×10^9 years, though there is clearly some scope for uncertainty.

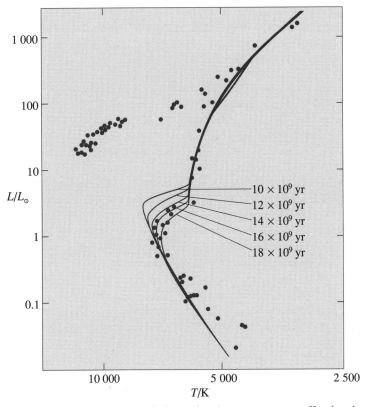

Figure 1.25 Theoretical predictions of main sequence turn-off points in globular clusters of various ages, compared with observational data from one particular cluster (M92).

At the time of writing, the ages of globular clusters are a matter of great interest. The problems of determining the accurate ages of the clusters have still not been solved and it is difficult to be more precise than saying that they are generally thought to be in the range 10×10^9 to 17×10^9 years. However, there has been some progress with the question of the relative ages of different clusters. A number of recent studies have indicated that some of the halo clusters are several billion years older than others. If this is correct, it indicates that the formation of the halo was not, as was once thought, the result of the rapid collapse of a galaxy-sized gas cloud over just a few tens of million years. Either the collapse was a much more gradual process or it didn't happen at all. It has been suggested that the halo may have been formed by the coalescence of many different cloudlets and that globular clusters formed either in these cloudlets or in collisions between them. If so, the apparent range of globular cluster ages would indicate the timescale of this entire process.

1.4.3 The gaseous corona

The halo is devoid of giant molecular cloud complexes, bright HII regions and all the other gaseous symptoms of star formation. As shown in TV programme 6, observations carried out by radio astronomers, working at wavelengths near 21 cm, have revealed the presence of clouds of atomic hydrogen well away from the plane of the Galaxy. It is difficult to determine the distance of these clouds but they are known to be moving rapidly relative to the Sun so they are referred to as **high-velocity clouds**.

☐ How could the speed of such clouds be determined?

■ By looking for a shift in the wavelength (or frequency) of the 21 cm line and assuming that it is a Doppler effect due to the motion of the cloud. Many of the high-velocity clouds have significant blueshifts, so they must have a large radial component of velocity *towards* the Sun.

The origin of the high-velocity clouds is something of a mystery (note that they are quite distinct from the high-velocity *stars* mentioned in Section 1.2, which are stars typical of the halo that are passing through the disc at high velocity). One recent suggestion is that they are fragments of an expanding shell of gas created by an enormous explosion that occurred in the Perseus spiral arm (see Figure 1.13) about 7×10^6 years ago. However, other interpretations have been suggested, many of which are still viable.

Apart from the high-velocity clouds, gravity seems to have pulled most of the atomic and molecular hydrogen of the Milky Way into a relatively thin disc around the mid-plane of the Galaxy. However, as you saw in Chapter 5 of Book 1, the much hotter *ionized* gas of the hot intercloud medium is more extensively distributed. A good deal of this ionized gas is to be found in the halo, though its density is very low and its precise distribution is very uncertain.

The body of hot gas in the halo is sometimes referred to as the **gaseous corona**. Its existence was predicted in the mid-1950s, long before it was first directly observed. The prediction was made by Lyman Spitzer (1914–), a leading expert on the interstellar medium, who realized that a Galactic corona of very hot gas was necessary to stop the high-velocity clouds from dissipating into space. The mechanism whereby such hot gas could be produced was something of an enigma, but it was proposed that a so-called **Galactic fountain** might be responsible. According to this proposal, supernovae taking place in the disc of the Galaxy could heat bubbles of coronal gas close to the disc to temperatures of 10^6 K or more. These bubbles would move away from the disc – displacing cooler denser overlying gas – as part of a convective flow thousands of parsecs across. Figure 1.26 tries to convey an impression of the overall effect, but it is highly schematic. It has been suggested that the high-velocity clouds might be part of the 'return leg' of this Galactic fountain.

Direct confirmation of Spitzer's prediction of a gaseous corona did not come until the late 1970s, following the launch of the astronomical satellite International Ultraviolet Explorer (IUE). Free of the limitations of the Earth's atmosphere, this satellite recorded the UV spectra of many stars in the Milky Way and beyond. Spitzer himself had predicted that coronal gas would produce characteristic absorption lines at UV wavelengths, and these were duly observed – many of them at wavelengths below 200 nm. A part of a UV stellar spectrum, showing coronal absorption is illustrated in Figure 1.27.

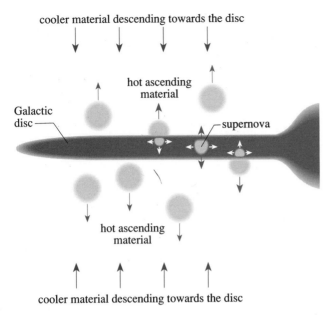

cooler material descending towards the disc

cooler material descending towards the disc

Figure 1.26   The Galactic fountain heating the tenuous coronal gas.

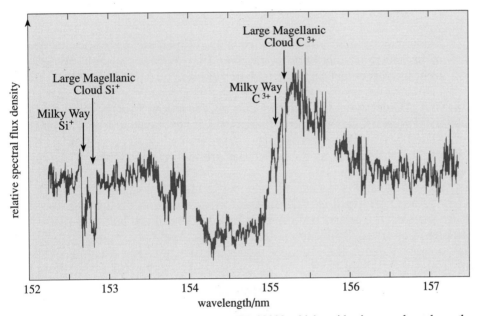

Figure 1.27   Part of the spectrum of the star HD 38282 which resides in a nearby galaxy, the Large Magellanic Cloud. The spectrum shows two pairs of absorption features (arrowed); one pair due to ionized silicon (Si^+), the other due to triply ionized carbon (C^{3+}). In each case, the shorter-wavelength member of the pair is due to absorption in the corona of the Milky Way. The longer-wavelength member is due to similar absorption in the Large Magellanic Cloud, but it has been Doppler-shifted due to the relative motion of the two galaxies.

Finally, something should be said about the dark matter, which can only be detected indirectly by its gravitational influence. It is widely expected that the halo contains a substantial amount of dark matter, though little is known about its nature or distribution. Dark matter may be co-extensive with the halo or may well extend far beyond the boundaries of the halo. At the risk of some confusion, many authors now refer to the outlying dark matter as the dark halo or even just the halo. We therefore prefer the term **dark envelope** since it avoids confusion. It goes without saying that the directly-detectable halo that has been the subject of this section should not be confused with this hypothetical dark envelope.

1   The Galactic halo is the most extensive of the directly detectable structural components of the Milky Way. It is an ancient and relatively inactive part of the Galaxy.

2   The shape and size of the halo are difficult to determine. Its shape is roughly spherical but it is thought that there might be a considerable amount of polar flattening, resulting in an oblate spheroidal shape. There is some evidence that its diameter is about 40 kpc though it might be much larger.

3   The main constituents of the halo are old, low-metallicity stars of population II. The total mass of these stars is about $10^9 M_\odot$.

4   About 1% of the halo stars are contained in ancient globular clusters. These are tight spherical swarms of stars up to about 50 pc across and containing 10^5–10^6 members. Their ages may be determined (with some difficulty) from their H–R diagrams and are generally in the range 10×10^9 to 17×10^9 years.

5   The halo includes a corona of tenuous, hot (10^6 K or more) gas. This is thought to be heated by a Galactic fountain powered by supernovae and helps to confine high-velocity clouds of atomic hydrogen.

6   There may be an extensive dark envelope of dark matter but little is known of its nature or distribution, and even its existence can only be deduced from indirect evidence, at the time of writing.

SAQ 1.11 (Objective 1.6)   No globular cluster has an H–R diagram like that shown in Figure 1.24a. What sort of object might have such an H–R diagram?

SAQ 1.12 (Objective 1.8)   What colour are the brightest stars in a globular cluster?

SAQ 1.13 (Objective 1.6)   Outline the ways in which the various forms of hydrogen gas (H_2, H and H^+) are distributed between the halo and disc of the Milky Way.

1.5   The nuclear bulge

As usual, this section opens with an overview of its topic – the nuclear bulge. This is followed by two short subsections, one describing the outer part of the bulge, the other the inner part.

1.5.1   An overview of the nuclear bulge

Evidence for the existence of a bulge in the Milky Way comes most directly from optical observations. Plate 3.3 shows a clear concentration of brightness, and a thickening of the Galactic disc, in one direction. The nuclear bulge is, though, the most enigmatic part of the Milky Way (apart, of course, from the elusive dark matter). Much of it is heavily obscured, particularly the central regions, which may well be the most interesting. The widest possible variety of techniques have been used to probe the central region, but the results are still fragmentary and the overall pattern unclear.

   What is certain is that no simple picture will explain all the features of the bulge. Containing, as it does, the meeting point of the densest parts of the halo and the disc, it might naturally be expected to show a wide variety of phenomena, but the addition of what seem to be its own intrinsic contributions makes the resulting region very complicated indeed.

On the one hand, the nuclear bulge contains a great deal of 'old' population II material; low-mass main sequence stars, red giants, planetary nebulae and so on. This has led some authors to treat the bulge as little more than the central concentration of the halo. On the other hand, the bulge contains the **Galactic centre**, a complex domain that includes a number of active star-forming regions. Globular clusters are concentrated there (Figure 1.22); both the low-metallicity halo globulars and the higher-metallicity disc globulars. The majority of bulge stars near the Galactic plane are probably older than the Sun, perhaps as old as the stars of the disc globulars, but many of them seem to have higher metallicity than the Sun. Perhaps this unusual combination of properties is to be expected in such an exotic location. The motions of stars in the bulge are also of interest. Unlike the disc, where stars revolve in an orderly fashion around the Galactic centre, the stars in the bulge appear to be moving randomly. In fact, their motions resemble those of stars in elliptical galaxies, which will be discussed in Chapter 2.

There is certainly a good deal of gas in the central region of the bulge. Molecular, atomic and ionized hydrogen have all been detected there, as will shortly be described. In addition, the emissions from various other molecules (e.g. CO and OH) have played an important part in contributing to our current understanding – such as it is. Investigations of the motion of the gas in the centre of the Galaxy are of particular interest since they provide insight into the level of activity there and they shed light on the distribution of mass causing those motions. The results of some of these investigations will be quoted in what follows, though discussion of the methods whereby such results are obtained will be mainly deferred to the next chapter.

Studies of the bulges of external galaxies, combined with the available information about the Milky Way, have led to the expectation that the bulge will be a slowly rotating oblate spheroid with an axis ratio c/a (similar to that defined for the halo in Figure 1.21) of about 0.7. If the bulge is spheroidal and does rotate as expected, then it is thought that the rotation speed of its outer regions will be approximately $100 \, \text{km s}^{-1}$, less than half that of the disc in the neighbourhood of the Sun (Figure 1.11). The equatorial radius of the bulge is about 3 kpc and its total mass perhaps around $10^{10} \, M_\odot$.

1.5.2 Approaching the Galactic centre

Many of the results quoted in this subsection and the one that follows were obtained using radio and infrared astronomy. TV programme 6 includes several images of the Galactic centre obtained by observing at these wavelengths.

If we could travel to the bulge and approach the Galactic centre, what would we encounter? The answer to this question is not known with any degree of certainty. From our vantage point, orbiting the Sun, we can only observe the bulge from one direction and even that view is badly obscured. Nonetheless, astronomers, particularly radio astronomers, have assiduously studied the two-dimensional view of the bulge that is available and they have used their expertise and experience to interpret this in terms of a three-dimensional model. This is a difficult and somewhat speculative undertaking – the data are sometimes ambiguous and some interpretations are adopted because they are more likely on the balance of probabilities, rather than because they are beyond all reasonable doubt. Nonetheless, the main purpose of this subsection is to introduce the chief features of the two-dimensional view and to describe their three-dimensional interpretation.

Optical views of the bulge are very limited, as already noted. One of the best is through a narrow 'tunnel' of relatively unobscured space – a sort of gap in the dust. This unusually clear region was exploited by Walter Baade in his studies of the stellar population of the bulge and is known as **Baade's window**. However even this line of sight is not totally clear and is directed about 4° away from the Galactic centre, so it doesn't allow a glimpse of the centre itself.

ITQ 1.8   Assuming that the Galactic centre is at a distance of 8.5 kpc, work out the physical distance, in the central region of the Galaxy, that corresponds to each of the following angular separations: 1°; 1 arcmin (= 1°/60); 1 arcsec (= 1°/3 600).

Fortunately, radio waves *are* able to penetrate the material that obscures the optical view, and they can provide a great deal of information. Radio astronomy provides information in essentially three different ways, as described below. TV programme 6 shows examples of all three of these approaches to using radio astrononomy.

Radio images

By working at a fixed wavelength and recording the intensity of emission in various directions, it is possible to build up a two-dimensional radio image of a region of space. This is rather like having a radio 'photograph'. It will indicate major features but will not provide much insight into what they are. An all-sky image of this kind, recorded at a wavelength of 73.5 cm is shown in Plate 3.4a. It gives no depth information, since it is purely a projection, and so gives a greatly exaggerated impression of the thickness of the disc.

Radio spectroscopy

By studying a particular feature over a range of wavelengths it is possible to determine its radio spectrum. Radio astronomers are used to dealing with such spectra and can use them, for example, to distinguish a supernova remnant from an HII region. Radio spectra consist of lines and a continuum – just like optical spectra. The techniques used to investigate radio 'lines' are fairly specialized and there tends to be something of a distinction between 'line studies' and 'continuum studies'. Like optical lines, radio line spectra can give a great deal of information about the types of molecules, atoms and ions present.

Doppler studies

This is essentially another aspect of radio spectroscopy. Due to the Doppler effect (introduced in Subsection 2.2.1 of Book 1) the wavelength at which a particular radio line is observed will be partly determined by the motion of the source of the emission. Thus, by observing a particular line (such as the 21 cm line due to neutral hydrogen) and measuring its Doppler shift along various lines of sight, it is possible to construct a plot showing the extent to which sources in a given direction are moving towards or away from the observer. Such plots give no *direct* indication of the distance of the source, though an experienced analyst may be able to deduce such information from various *indirect* indicators such as the way one feature overlaps another, and the data can be checked against (and so used to modify, or consolidate) an assumed model.

Largely on the basis of 21 cm hydrogen line studies that combine all three of the approaches, it is believed that a plan view of the inner parts of the Milky Way should look something like Figure 1.28. Remember, this is a 'biased' plan since it is based on 21 cm emission. (A photograph would be equally biased towards light-emitting features.) It seems that a journey towards the centre would take us through the Sagittarius arm and, on the boundaries of the nuclear bulge, through an outwardly expanding feature known as the **3 kpc arm** (approximately 3 kpc from the Galactic centre). The origin and nature of the 3 kpc arm, and of some other outward-moving hydrogen clouds a little further in, is unclear. Nonetheless, the general outward motion has led to speculation about the possibility of violent outbursts in the core of the Galaxy in the distant past.

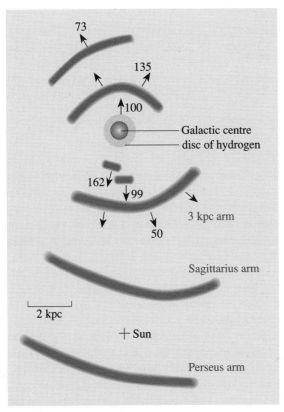

Figure 1.28   Schematic plan of the inner parts of the Milky Way, based on 21 cm hydrogen line emission. The numbers against the arrows refer to speeds in km s^{-1}.

Apart from the expanding arms, the most conspicuous feature of the nuclear bulge, seen at 21 cm, is a disc of atomic hydrogen near the centre of the Galaxy (Figure 1.29 shows a section, in Galactic coordinates). The radius of this **nuclear disc** seems to be about 600 pc and the total mass of atomic hydrogen within it has been estimated at about $4 \times 10^6 M_\odot$.

The nuclear disc is not restricted to the mid-plane of the Galaxy – it stretches a degree or so either side and seems to be inclined at a small angle, as indicated in Figure 1.29. The contents of this nuclear disc, apart from atomic hydrogen, are the subject of the next subsection.

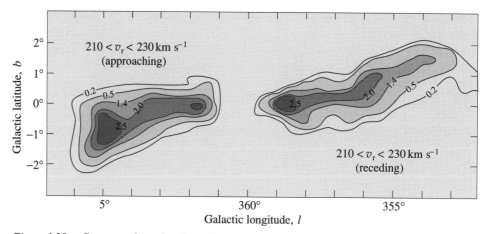

Figure 1.29 Contours of equal radio brightness in a narrow range of wavelengths near 21 cm. By limiting the wavelength range, the observations are effectively limited to a narrow range of speeds v_r (along the observer's line of sight) relative to the Galactic centre. The inclination of the disc is quite clear. (Note that this is a plot of Galactic longitude (l) versus Galactic latitude (b).)

1.5.3 The centre of the Milky Way

Observations made within the boundaries of the nuclear disc at wavelengths other than 21 cm reveal the presence of forms of matter other than atomic hydrogen close to the Galactic centre. Various radio lines due to molecules such as CO, OH and HCN are seen and it is clear that there are many molecular clouds. The molecular emission is patchy but Doppler studies indicate that there is an expanding ring-shaped region, about 75 pc thick and 300 pc in radius, that is particularly rich in molecules. More molecular clouds can be seen within this **molecular ring** and it seems that molecular hydrogen, which is generally sparse within the bulge, dominates the gaseous component in the central regions. Molecular hydrogen itself is not always easy to detect, so sometimes the relatively rare CO molecule (which is found in association with H_2 molecules) is used as a tracer since it has a bright radio line at 2.6 mm. Assuming that the ratio of carbon to hydrogen in the Galactic core is similar to that in the neighbourhood of the Sun, and that 10–20% of the carbon is in the form of CO, as expected, there would seem to be about $10^8 M_\odot$ of molecular hydrogen within 300 pc of the centre.

In addition to molecular line studies, observations of radio continuum and infrared emissions have revealed the existence of other features (mainly dense clouds) within the molecular ring. (Infrared images of features close to the Galactic centre can be seen in Plate 3.7b.) The general outcome of these observations is indicated, highly schematically, in Figure 1.30 which provides edge-on and (speculative) face-on views of the central region of the Milky Way. As you can see, the molecular ring is thought to be rotating at about 50 km s⁻¹ and expanding at 130 km s⁻¹, while many of the clouds within have their own characteristic velocities that have been tentatively associated with an overall rotation of the inner parts of the nuclear disc. This central region contains two features which are particularly prominent in radio continuum maps and were named Sagittarius A (Sgr A) and Sagittarius B2 (Sgr B₂) by the radio astronomers who discovered them. Sagittarius B2 is associated with a number of HII regions and is usually regarded as a star-forming region. Sagittarius A encloses the centre of the Milky Way and has been the subject of intensive investigation at many wavelengths.

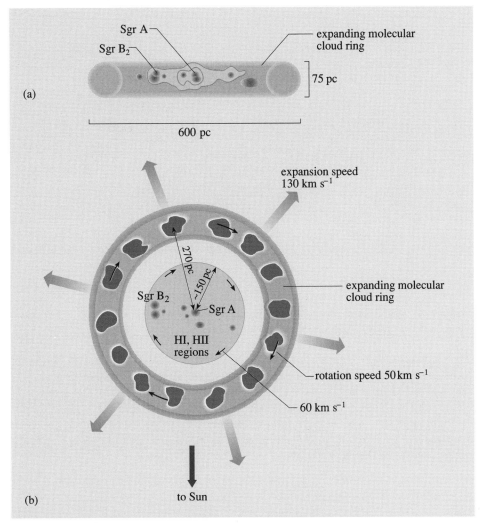

Figure 1.30 Highly schematic (a) edge-on and (b) face-on views of the molecular ring and its contents. These views make use of observations at a variety of wavelengths.

Figure 1.31 provides an edge-on view of the Galactic centre similar to that of Figure 1.30a, but on an even finer scale. In effect, we are zooming in on Sagittarius A and its immediate surroundings. Once again, several different kinds of observation have been put together to provide the diagram. The mysterious non-thermal **radio arc** (Figure 1.31) about 30 pc from the Galactic centre has been known since the 1950s, but only in the 1980s did 21 cm observations made at the Very Large Array (featured in TV programme 7) in New Mexico reveal that it consists of a set of fine parallel filaments each about 1 pc wide and 4 pc long, joined to the Galactic centre by other fine filaments. The significance of this feature is not clear, though it is often noted that its shape and structure are both suggestive of some sort of magnetic effect.

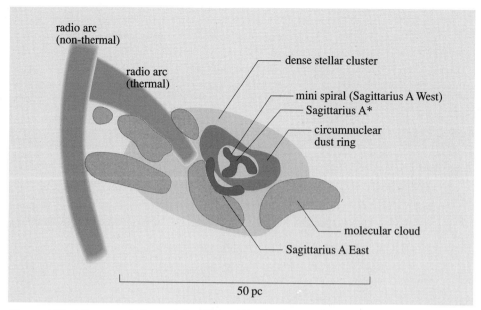

Figure 1.31 The central 50 pc of the Milky Way. The viewpoint is edgewise to the Galactic plane, i.e. as we on Earth look towards the Galactic centre.

The **circumnuclear dust ring** is the discovery of infrared astronomers, while the **mini spiral** (Plate 3.7c), is another radio discovery. In fact, despite appearances the mini spiral may not be a spiral at all. Doppler studies at points along the arms of the mini spiral support the suggestion (illustrated in Figure 1.32) that it is part of an inclined disc whirling around the intense, unresolved radio source known as **Sagittarius A*** (Sgr A*). It is this latter object which is thought to mark the precise centre of the Milky Way.

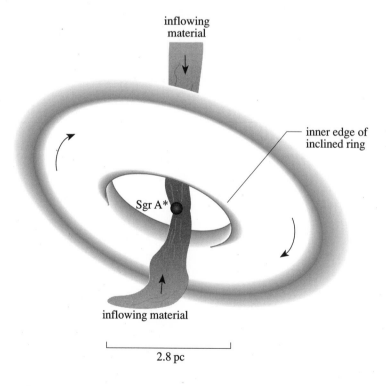

Figure 1.32 A possible interpretation of the mini spiral (the western part of the radio source Sagittarius A). Perhaps it consists of a rotating ring (the inner edge of a disc) and two inflowing streams.

A number of astronomers have interpreted the many unusual features of the Galactic centre as evidence for the existence of a very massive black hole right at the heart of the Milky Way. Furthermore, as mentioned earlier, it is possible to estimate the mass enclosed within a certain volume by observing the motion of material around that volume – provided the observed motion is the result of gravitational forces alone. In the case of the Galactic centre, such observations have been performed at various wavelengths using the emissions from a wide range of nuclear bulge sources. The resulting limits on the enclosed mass within spherical regions of various radii, centred on the Galactic centre, are shown in Figure 1.33. As you can see, something like $3 \times 10^6 \, M_\odot$ is contained within 0.2 pc of the centre. Various interpretations are still possible but the proposal that the enclosed mass takes the form of a black hole, probably not much bigger than the Sun, with a mass of $10^6 \, M_\odot$ or so, has many adherents. Only time will tell if it is correct.

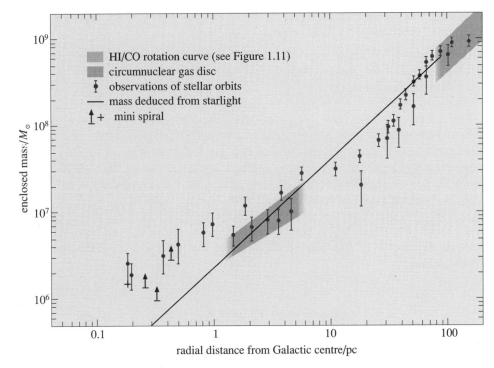

Figure 1.33 The mass enclosed within spherical volumes of various radii, centred on the Galactic centre. (All but one of the points labelled mini spiral are lower limits of the measurements. These lower limits are denoted by an arrow pointing upward from the bar.)

Summary of Section 1.5 and SAQs

1 The nuclear bulge is the most enigmatic part of the Milky Way due to the high level of optical obscuration. Most of what we know about the nuclear bulge, particularly about its most central parts, has been learned from radio and infrared studies.

2 The bulge seems to be a spheroid of equatorial diameter about 6 kpc. Its outer regions rotate at about 100 km s^{-1} and its total mass is around $10^{10} \, M_\odot$.

3 The bulge mainly consists of population II stars, though their metallicities seem to be unusually high in many cases. Ancient halo globulars are concentrated in and around the bulge, as are the apparently more youthful disc globulars. Stars appear to move randomly within the bulge.

4 All forms of gaseous hydrogen (molecular, atomic and ionized) have been detected in the bulge, as have many other gases (CO, OH and HCN for instance). In the central regions of the bulge, the dominant gas seems to be molecular hydrogen.

5 Within the bulge a number of different features can be identified. These features have 'conventional' interpretations though these interpretations are not always unambiguous. Well-known features include the 3 kpc arm, the nuclear disc and molecular ring, and the continuum radio sources Sagittarius A and Sagittarius B2.

6 Sagittarius A surrounds the centre of the Milky Way. At its heart lies the unresolved radio source Sagittarius A*.

7 Attempts have been made to interpret Sagittarius A* as a black hole of mass $10^6 M_\odot$ or more. Such attempts might be able to account for the various signs of energetic activity in the centre of the Galaxy, though other interpretations are still possible.

8 The study of the centre of the Milky Way provides another excellent example of the value of studying a particular object or region at many different wavelengths.

SAQ 1.14 (Objective 1.9)   Suppose that Sagittarius A* does not contain a massive black hole but rather, as some astronomers have suggested, consists of a dense cluster of stars. Assuming that this central cluster consists of a fairly uniform distribution of $10 M_\odot$ stars filling a spherical volume of radius 1.0 pc, estimate the average separation of stars that would be consistent with current beliefs about the mass enclosed in that region.

SAQ 1.15 (Objective 1.9)   How could the existence of a very massive black hole at the centre of the Galaxy account for the *emission* of radiation from Sagittarius A*?

Objectives for Chapter 1

After studying Chapter 1 (and any associated audio, video or TV material) you should be able to:

1.1   Give brief definitions of the terms, concepts and principles listed below.

1.2   Describe general features of the Milky Way, including the major structural components and the main constituents.

1.3   Recall from memory the (estimated) sizes of the main structural components and the relative proportions of the major constituents.

1.4   Sketch the rotation curve of the Milky Way, comment on the uncertainties associated with such a sketch, and explain the role of the curve in attempts to assess the mass of the Milky Way.

1.5   Identify the approximate location of the Sun in relation to the overall structure of the Milky Way and outline the observational evidence supporting the view that the Milky Way is a spiral galaxy.

1.6   Describe a variety of prominent features of the Milky Way, including OB associations, open clusters and globular clusters. Outline their distribution as observed from the Earth, and comment on some of the difficulties of making observations from within the disc of the Milky Way.

1.7 Outline the major features of the density wave theory that is thought to account for the presence of spiral arms in the disc of the Galaxy.

1.8 Recognize various features in the globular cluster H–R diagram and explain the particular significance of the main sequence turn-off point.

1.9 Outline the results and possible implications of studies of the Galactic centre at a variety of wavelengths.

1.10 Describe the contents of the nuclear bulge, particularly its central regions.

List of scientific terms, concepts and principles used in Chapter 1

Term	Page	Term	Page	Term	Page
3 kpc arm	41	Galactic longitude	21	OB association	29
Baade's window	40	Galactic magnetic field	10	open cluster	28
barred spiral galaxy	9	Galactic plane	21	Orion arm	22
baryonic matter	8	Galactic spheroid	8	population I	11
circumnuclear dust ring	44	gaseous corona	36	population II	11
co-rotation radius	26	globular cluster	33	radio arc	43
dark envelope	37	Gould's belt	22	rotation curve	15
dark matter	7	halo (of a spiral)	8	Sagittarius A*	44
density wave theory	25	high-velocity clouds	36	self-sustaining star formation	28
differential rotation	14	high-velocity stars	12	sequential star formation	28
disc (of a spiral)	8	Local Bubble	23	spheroid	32
disc globulars	33	Local System	23	spiral arm	8
Galactic centre	39	main sequence turn-off point	34	spiral density wave	25
Galactic coordinates	21	mini spiral	44	structural components (of a galaxy)	7
Galactic equator	21	molecular ring	42	thick disc	20
Galactic fountain	36	nuclear bulge	8	winding dilemma	25
Galactic latitude	21	nuclear disc	41		

Chapter 2
Beyond the Milky Way – other galaxies

Prepared for the Course Team by Bob Lambourne and Liz Swinbank

Contents

2.1 Introduction

Despite its vast size the Milky Way occupies only a tiny part of the visible Universe. This simple observation raises the question, 'What, if anything, lies beyond the boundaries of our own galaxy?' Until the 1920s the answer was uncertain, but we now know that the correct response is: 'Other galaxies – thousands of millions of them'. These other galaxies – sometimes called *external galaxies*, to emphasize the fact that they lie *beyond* the confines of the Milky Way – can be broadly divided into two classes. The majority of them belong to the class of so-called **normal galaxies**, which have a more-or-less unvarying luminosity that is roughly accounted for by the stars and interstellar matter that they contain. A minority of external galaxies – perhaps 2%, though it is very difficult to be precise – belong to a different class, that of **active galaxies**, characterized by an unusually high (and possibly variable) luminosity that appears to be largely non-stellar in origin. This chapter is concerned with normal external galaxies; the more specialized subject of active galaxies will be explored in Chapter 3.

The text of this chapter is divided into four major sections. The first deals with the classification of galaxies according to their shape and certain other readily apparent characteristics. This subject was pioneered by the great American astronomer Edwin P. Hubble (1889–1953) (Figure 2.1) in the 1920s and it is a version of Hubble's classification scheme that will provide the basis for our own discussion. The second major section concentrates on the determination of the distances of galaxies, which is a difficult undertaking, but one of great importance since it holds the key to many other issues, including the extent to which galaxies gather together in groups or clusters. The third major section is concerned with the determination of a range of important properties of galaxies, such as mass, luminosity, stellar content and so on. The fourth, and final, major section contains various observations about the origin and evolution of galaxies, a complex and perplexing field of study which is widely regarded as the greatest challenge facing the current generation of astronomers and astrophysicists.

Figure 2.1 Edwin P. Hubble (1889–1953), a leading figure in the development of galactic astronomy.

In addition to the text, this chapter is supported by video sequence 10 *A radio astronomy project*. This sequence uses ideas about rotation that you met in relation to the Milky Way in Chapter 1 and applies them to other galaxies. You should view the sequence, and work through the project, when you are in Subsection 2.4.2 since that is where you will deal with the rotation of other galaxies.

Note on terminology

The term 'galactic astronomy' (as opposed to 'extra-galactic astronomy') is often used to refer to the astronomical study of the Milky Way and thus excludes the study of other galaxies. Because of this usage, terms such as 'galactic distance' and 'galactic mass' have to be used with caution since some readers might interpret them as referring specifically to the Milky Way. To avoid this potential confusion some authors use the terms 'galaxian distance' and 'galaxian mass' when referring to galaxies other than the Milky Way. We shall *not* follow this convention. In this text the term 'galactic' should be taken to refer to galaxies in general. However, when specific reference to the Milky Way is intended we shall follow the convention of Chapter 1 by spelling Galactic with a capital G. Thus, the term 'galactic centre' would refer to the centre of any galaxy under discussion, whereas 'Galactic centre' would refer specifically to the centre of the Milky Way.

2.2 The classification of galaxies

2.2.1 The Hubble classification

The annual meeting of the American National Academy of Sciences held at the Smithsonian Institute in Washington DC in April 1920 is widely regarded as a major event in the history of astronomy. This meeting was the scene of what has become known as 'Astronomy's Great Debate', in which Harlow Shapley (whose work on the distribution of globular clusters was described in Chapter 1) and Heber D. Curtis (1872–1942) took opposing views on two fundamental issues: the determination of the size of the Milky Way, and the existence of external galaxies beyond the Milky Way. Shapley believed that the Milky Way was very large and occupied more-or-less the entire Universe, whereas Curtis favoured the idea that it was just one galaxy among many.

By 1930 these two issues, which had so greatly perplexed the astronomers of 1920, had been settled. Shapley's method of working out the size of the Milky Way had been widely accepted (though the value it provided was substantially revised in the 1950s) and the existence of external galaxies had been definitively established by Edwin Hubble (as will be described in the next section). Indeed, by that time so many external galaxies were known that it had already become customary to divide them into a number of different classes, according to their **morphology**, i.e. their apparent shape and structure. One reason for classification is convenience: it provides a shorthand way of referring to galaxies that seem to have something in common. But classification is a more useful tool than a mere labelling system. In order to understand the physical properties of galaxies (their motions, their star formation, their evolution, for example) we have to rely on their observational properties which, we hope, may be related to the underlying physics. By a detailed study of a relatively small number of objects we hope to learn something about the class in general.

A **classification scheme** used for galaxies was first introduced by Hubble, in 1926. A more recent version of the **Hubble classes** is shown in Figure 2.2. Though various modifications and extensions have been proposed, this still represents the basic classification scheme in use today. As you can see, the scheme recognizes four major classes of galaxy; **elliptical**, **lenticular**, **spiral** and **irregular**, with both the lenticular and spiral classes being subdivided into **barred** and **unbarred** varieties. In addition, the various classes and subclasses are divided into a number of **Hubble types** (Figure 2.2) each of which is denoted by a combination of letters and numbers.

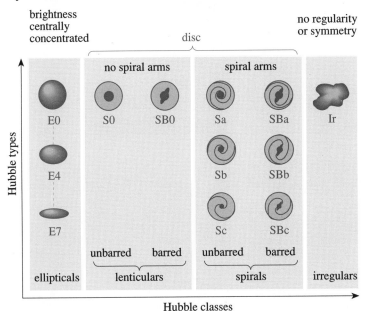

Figure 2.2 The Hubble classification scheme for galaxies.

The Hubble classification is of great importance in galactic astronomy, and there are indeed physical as well as observational differences between the various types and classes. But how are the classes and types defined? There are several important questions to ask when determining the Hubble class:

- Is there any overall regularity or symmetry?
- Is the light concentrated in the centre?
- Is there a disc?
- Are there spiral arms?

As discussed below, answering these questions puts a galaxy into one of the main Hubble classes. Other observational properties are then used to assign a galaxy to one of the types within its main class.

Elliptical galaxies

Elliptical galaxies are characterized by an overall elliptical outline when viewed in the sky, and a generally featureless appearance, combined with a light output that is highly concentrated in the galactic centre and decreases steadily with increasing distance from the centre. These are divided into Hubble types that range from E0 for those which appear as circles to E7 for the most elongated (Figure 2.2). The integer that follows the E in each type designation is the nearest whole number to the value of ten times the **flattening factor** $f = (a - b)/a$, where the **semi-major axis**, a, and **semi-minor axis**, b, of the observed ellipse are defined in Figure 2.3. The lack of elliptical galaxies with flattening factors greater than 0.7 probably indicates that such highly flattened ellipticals are unstable. Photographic images of various types of elliptical galaxy are shown in Figure 2.4, while Plate 3.9b uses (false) colour to indicate the decrease of light output

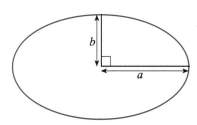

Figure 2.3 The semi-major axis, a, and the semi-minor axis, b, of an ellipse.

51

with increasing distance from the galactic centre. Note that elliptical galaxies are assigned a Hubble type according to their (visually) *observed* shapes; the scheme takes no account of their 'true' shape as three-dimensional objects (unlike spirals, which are classified according to what they would look like if viewed 'face-on'). Also, their shapes observed using other wavelengths may be different.

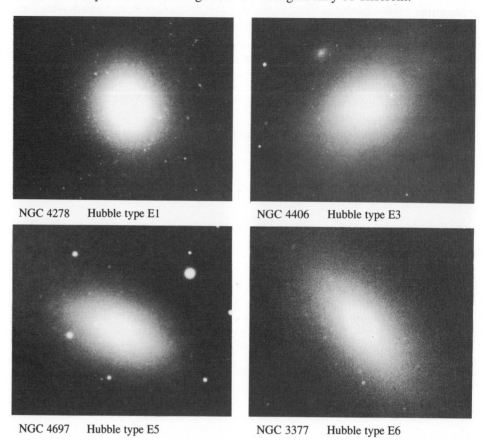

NGC 4278   Hubble type E1

NGC 4406   Hubble type E3

NGC 4697   Hubble type E5

NGC 3377   Hubble type E6

Figure 2.4 Elliptical galaxies of various Hubble types. (*Note*: NGC stands for the New General Catalogue of Nebulae and Clusters (of stars), published in 1888 by Johan Dreyer. Many of the objects classified in the NGC are now known to be galaxies – but in 1888 the existence of galaxies beyond the Milky way was unrecognized.)

Spiral galaxies

The light of spiral galaxies is much less centrally concentrated than is the case for ellipticals. Spiral galaxies are characterized by a disc and a nuclear bulge, and the disc contains spiral arms. In some spirals the arms are long and continuous while in others they are broken or fragmented and, consequently, difficult to follow in detail despite an overall impression of spiral structure. (It may well be that the Milky Way is of this latter sort.) Spiral galaxies are divided into two subclasses according to whether or not they have a central bar, and each subclass is further divided into types Sa, Sb, Sc or SBa, SBb, SBc according to the openness of the arms and the relative size of the bulge (Figure 2.2). Spirals of types Sa and SBa have tightly wound arms and a relatively large bulge; those of types Sc and SBc have loosely wound arms and a relatively small bulge. Galaxies that cannot be unambiguously assigned to one type are classified as a combination of the two nearest types – for example, a galaxy that is intermediate between Sa and Sb is denoted Sab.

Lenticular galaxies

As their name implies, these are lens-shaped galaxies. Like spirals they have a disc and a nuclear bulge – but no spiral arms. The bulge may be quite large in comparison to the disc (much more so, on average, than in the case of the Milky Way for instance) and may take the form of a spheroid – as in the S0 type – or may be elongated into a 'bar' as in the SB0 type. Lenticular galaxies are often seen as an intermediate class between ellipticals and spirals. However, some have relatively small nuclear bulges, so lenticulars are often treated as a third subclass of spirals in addition to barred and unbarred. They are sometimes described as 'armless spirals'. This is really a contradiction in terms, but it conveys the right impression to a reader such as yourself who is already familiar with a spiral galaxy like the Milky Way.

Photographic images of various types of lenticular and spiral galaxy are shown in Figure 2.5, and various types of spiral galaxies are shown in Plate 3.8. It should be noted that although the diagrams in Figure 2.2 show spiral galaxies face-on and with two spiral arms apiece, the observed spirals will normally be inclined relative to the observer and may have more than two arms.

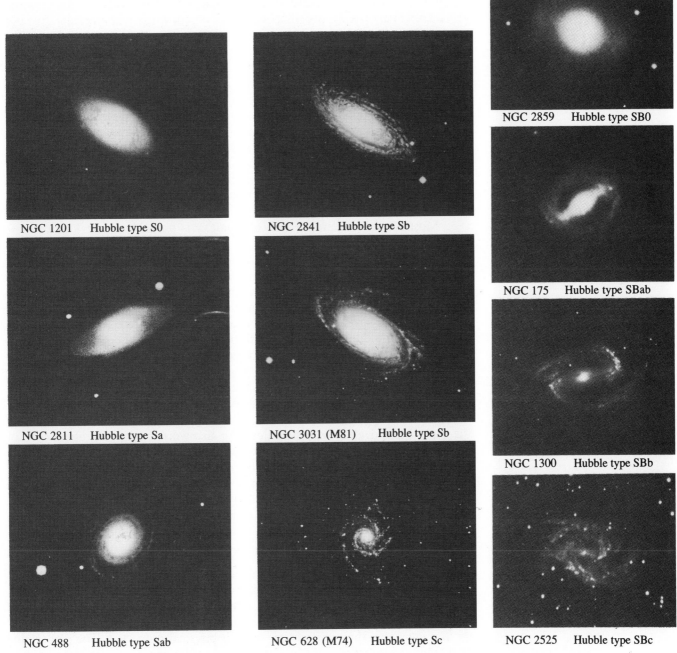

NGC 1201   Hubble type S0

NGC 2841   Hubble type Sb

NGC 2859   Hubble type SB0

NGC 2811   Hubble type Sa

NGC 3031 (M81)   Hubble type Sb

NGC 175   Hubble type SBab

NGC 488   Hubble type Sab

NGC 628 (M74)   Hubble type Sc

NGC 1300   Hubble type SBb

NGC 2525   Hubble type SBc

Figure 2.5   Lenticular (S0, SB0) and spiral galaxies of various Hubble types, both (a) unbarred and (b) barred (B in type label).

On the basis of our (rather poor) estimate of the external appearance of our own galaxy, it is traditional to describe the Milky Way as a galaxy of Hubble type Sb or Sc (or Sbc for short), though, as noted in Chapter 1, there is some suggestion that we are actually living in a barred, rather than an unbarred, spiral.

☐　If the Milky Way is a barred spiral, how would you write its Hubble type?

■　SBb or SBc (or SBbc for short).

Irregular galaxies

As you would expect, these galaxies (class Ir) show little sign of symmetry or regularity. Some have bar-like structures and some show vague signs of spiral arms. Others are totally irregular. Beautiful colour images of irregular galaxies can be seen in Plate 3.10.

Before leaving the topic of the Hubble scheme, it should be noted that classifying galaxies is not as unambiguous as it may seem from the above discussion and Figure 2.2. First, some aspects are somewhat subjective, and different observers may classify the same object differently. In the case of galaxies with discs, it can be difficult to distinguish between lenticulars and various types of spiral when the angle of inclination is large and the galaxy is almost edge-on. A more serious problem is that the visual appearance may be affected by such things as exposure time. For example, a short-exposure image of the elliptical galaxy in Plate 3.9a will show only the bright central parts, while a longer exposure will reveal the outer parts as well and give a different impression of the overall shape.

Most people's mental picture of a galaxy is probably a spiral, since these are the most photogenic and tend to predominate in illustrated books on astronomy (including *Images of the Cosmos*). However, over 60% of galaxies are ellipticals (faint **dwarf elliptical** galaxies, with masses around $10^6 M_\odot$, are in fact the most common type of galaxy), fewer than 30% are spirals and fewer than 15% irregulars. These figures are subject to some variation according to how the sample being surveyed is selected: there are relatively more E and S0 galaxies in regions where galaxies are more densely clustered together, and in the most densely clustered regions S, SB and Ir galaxies are almost totally absent. In any survey, it is important to eliminate bias: if only the most easily-observable galaxies are surveyed (i.e. those with the greatest apparent brightness), then the faint dwarf ellipticals will be under-represented, and the biased sample obtained will give the impression that there are relatively fewer ellipticals than is actually the case. While dealing with statistics, it is also worth noting that about 60% of spirals and lenticulars are barred, and that as well as influencing the appearance of a galaxy the presence of a bar may be related to stability.

Finally, it should be noted that about 1% of normal galaxies cannot be assigned to any of the Hubble classes in Figure 2.2, even if their shape is known. Some of these cases will be discussed briefly at the end of this section.

2.2.2　*The physical characteristics of the Hubble classes*

It is interesting that the range of galactic shapes is so limited that the great majority of galaxies can be assigned to one or another of the Hubble classes. However, it would be even more interesting to know the physical significance of such assignments. Surely, galaxies that differ in shape as radically as an E3 and an SBc must also show differences in their physical properties. The exploration of these intrinsic physical differences (as opposed to mere shapes) is the purpose of this subsection.

It has occasionally been suggested that the Hubble classification reveals an evolutionary sequence. In the past, some proponents of this idea believed that newly-formed galaxies were elliptical and that they flattened and developed into spirals with the passage of time. The diagram that is traditionally drawn to show the classification (and is used at the start of Part 3 in *Images of the Cosmos*) suggests an apparent progression through the Hubble classes. This evolutionary view is now totally rejected. The current belief is that the Hubble class of a galaxy is mainly determined by the environment in which it formed (although, as you will see in Section 2.5, the origin and formation of galaxies is still something of a mystery). There may be some subsequent evolution (as will be described later) but even this is not thought to involve a steady progression through the Hubble classes.

Despite the lack of evolutionary progression, galaxies do have physical properties that show systematic variations with Hubble class or type. One such property is rotation. On the whole, elliptical galaxies rotate slowly and, consequently, have very little angular momentum per unit mass. This is also the case for irregulars. Spirals and lenticulars rotate more rapidly and have correspondingly greater angular momentum per unit mass. For spiral galaxies of a given mass, angular momentum increases through the types Sa, Sb, Sc (or SBa, SBb, SBc).

Another property correlated with Hubble class is the proportion by mass of gas to stars in a galaxy. In the case of the Milky Way, this proportion is about 10% (see Chapter 1). In contrast, many ellipticals and lenticulars have scarcely any gas at all, so the proportion is very low for them (1% say). The proportion increases through the spiral classes Sa to Sc (or SBa to SBc) and is typically in the range 15–25% in irregulars. The presence or absence of gas is related to a number of other important distinguishing features of the various Hubble classes.

ITQ 2.1 Considering the variation of gas content with Hubble class, describe and explain any systematic variations you would expect to find between elliptical and spiral galaxies with regard to the following properties: presence of high-mass main sequence stars; proportion of stars in open clusters; prevalence of HII regions; abundance of population I stars relative to population II stars.

A number of other important galactic properties – such as mass, luminosity and diameter (the determination of which will be discussed later) – show wide variation in value from one galaxy to another, even within a given class. Because of the individual variations, these properties cannot be simply correlated with Hubble class. However, the *range* of variation of each of these properties *can* be so correlated – at least loosely. In general terms, spiral galaxies have a fairly narrow range of mass, luminosity and diameter (masses, for example are usually in the range from about $10^9 M_\odot$ to a few times $10^{12} M_\odot$), while elliptical galaxies cover a much wider range (masses of ellipticals vary from about $10^5 M_\odot$ to somewhat over $10^{13} M_\odot$). Irregular galaxies exhibit an intermediate range of properties (roughly 10^7–$10^{10} M_\odot$ in mass – even the largest irregulars less than a quarter of the mass of the Milky Way).

Another topic which merits discussion in this subsection is that of the true shape of elliptical galaxies. The fact that the Hubble types E0–E7 are based on 'apparent' (i.e. projected, two-dimensional) shape rather than 'true' (three-dimensional) shape raises a number of questions about elliptical galaxies. An elliptical galaxy must be an **ellipsoid** of some form, since that is the only shape that appears elliptical irrespective of the direction from which it is viewed. But is it an **oblate spheroid**, a **prolate spheroid**, or a **triaxial ellipsoid**? As Figure 2.6 shows, a triaxial ellipsoid has three unequal axes, while a spheroid has two equal axes, and cross-sections parallel to those axes are circular. Viewing a spheroid from various angles could give the whole E0–E7 range. Is it possible that all elliptical galaxies are the same shape? Before these questions were properly investigated it was more-or-less tacitly assumed that ellipticals actually had the shape of an oblate spheroid (i.e. a flattened sphere, as in Figure 2.6a). Furthermore, it was generally assumed that the galaxy rotated about the shortest axis and that the flattening was mainly due to this rotation – like the polar flattening of the Earth.

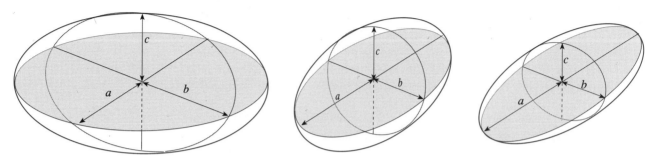

Figure 2.6 An ellipsoid is a three-dimensional body that appears to be elliptical from every direction. The shape of any particular ellipsoid can be specified by assigning lengths to the so-called principal semi-axes a, b and c shown in the diagram. (a) An oblate spheroid has $a = b > c$. (b) A prolate spheroid has $a = b < c$. (c) A triaxial ellipsoid has $a > b > c$.

Detailed studies of elliptical galaxies now indicate that these assumptions are not always justified. In some cases the observed motions of stars in elliptical galaxies are simply not consistent with a spheroidal distribution, and (particularly in the most luminous ellipticals) the rotations are often too slow to produce the flattenings. Moreover, some elliptical galaxies appear to be rotating about an axis other than the shortest axis, so their flattening is almost certainly *not* due to rotation. Another peculiarity that besets some ellipticals is that the elliptical contours of equal luminosity do not have a common major axis – there appears to be some sort of 'twist' in the heart of the galaxy. In view of these findings the simple spheroidal model of elliptical galaxies cannot be trusted, so the safest statement to make about the shapes of elliptical galaxies at the present time is that at least some are triaxial, though it is still quite possible that many are spheroidal.

Interestingly, it is now possible to use computer simulations to investigate **dynamical evolution**; that is, changes brought about by the host of gravitational interactions in a galaxy that change stellar orbits and velocities. Such studies indicate that triaxial distributions of stars may evolve into oblate spheroids and that the time taken for this evolution to occur increases with the size of the galaxy, but that some triaxial distributions of stars are stable provided the galactic rotation is fairly slow. Dynamical evolution is discussed further in Section 2.5, when we deal with the evolution of galaxies in more detail.

It would be an oversimplification if this section were to end without some reference to those galaxies that cannot be fitted into the Hubble classes shown in Figure 2.2, and others that can only be accommodated with difficulty. Various amendments and extensions to the Hubble scheme have therefore been proposed that reflect more accurately the true range of galactic shapes. It would be inappropriate to discuss this subject in great detail, but some indication of the limitations and shortcomings of the basic scheme will be of value.

Many galaxies have a more-or-less readily apparent Hubble type apart from the presence of some kind of abnormal feature. A case in point is the giant galaxy M87 seen in the constellation of Virgo – the subject of Plate 3.21 and featuring in TV programme 7. A medium-exposure photograph indicates that M87 is a straightforward elliptical of type E0 (or possibly E1). However, a short exposure, which emphasizes the central regions of the galaxy, shows an unusual feature – a 'jet' of material apparently spurting out from the core. Because of the presence of this jet, M87 is said to be a **peculiar galaxy** and is classified as having Hubble type E0p; the final 'p' indicating the presence of a peculiarity. A jet is not the only feature that can make a galaxy peculiar. Many peculiar galaxies appear to have been distorted in gravitational encounters with other galaxies: all interacting galaxies are peculiar. Some examples of interacting galaxies are shown in Figure 2.7.

viewing after Chapter 4, includes some examples of intVideo sequence 12, scheduled for eracting galaxies.

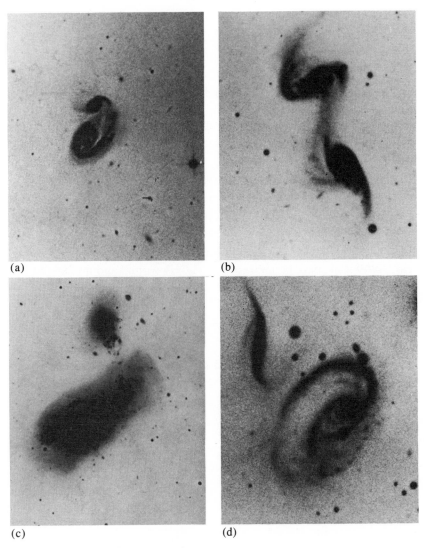

(a)

(b)

(c)

(d)

Figure 2.7   Some interacting galaxies.

Another sort of galaxy worth mentioning briefly here is the so-called **cD galaxy**. The 'c' indicates that these are supergiant systems, while the 'D' indicates an elliptical with a large diffuse envelope. In fact, cD galaxies are often found at the densely packed centres of large clusters of galaxies, and it may be that they are the result of the merger of several other galaxies. Detailed studies of some cD galaxies reveal the presence of several bright spots near the centre. These are sometimes interpreted as the nuclei of galaxies that have already been absorbed and are taken to be further evidence in favour of the merger hypothesis.

There are other revisions and extensions of the Hubble scheme but these will not be described here, however, because they play no part in the remainder of Block 3.

Summary of Section 2.2 and SAQs

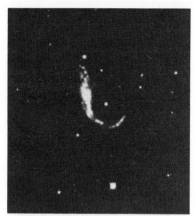

(a) NGC 7479

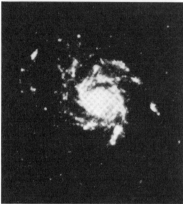

(b) NGC 5457 (M101)

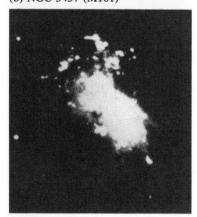

(c) NGC 4449

Figure 2.8 For use with SAQ 2.2.

1 Mainly according to their shape, most galaxies can be assigned to four different classes: elliptical, lenticular, spiral and irregular.

2 In the modified form of the Hubble classification scheme, shown in Figure 2.2, the spirals and lenticulars can be subdivided into barred and unbarred subclasses. The spirals can be further divided into a number of Hubble types. The ellipticals are also divided into a number of Hubble types.

3 Elliptical galaxies are essentially ellipsoidal distributions of old (population II) stars, almost devoid of gas and dust. Their three-dimensional shape is difficult to determine, but some at least appear to be triaxial ellipsoids with very little rotation. Some of the smaller ellipticals may well be oblate spheroids.

4 Lenticular galaxies appear to be an intermediate class between the most flattened of elliptical galaxies and the most tightly wound spirals. They show clear signs of a disc and a central bulge, but they have no spiral arms and little interstellar gas.

5 Spiral galaxies have a disc, a central bulge and often a central bar. Within this class, spiral arms may be more-or-less tightly wound and the bulge may be more-or-less prominent in relation to the disc. (The Milky Way is a spiral galaxy, probably of Hubble type Sb or Sc, and may have a bar.)

6 Irregular galaxies are generally chaotic and asymmetric, though some exhibit a bar and others show some traces of spiral structure.

7 The largest normal galaxies are the cD galaxies – giant ellipticals which may have been formed in mergers and which are often found close to the centres of clusters of galaxies.

8 Over 60% of galaxies are ellipticals, fewer than 30% are spirals, and fewer than 15% irregulars. Dwarf ellipticals are the most common type.

SAQ 2.1 (Objective 2.2)   If the ellipse shown in Figure 2.3 represented the outline of an elliptical galaxy, what would be its Hubble type?

SAQ 2.2 (Objective 2.2)   Figure 2.8 shows three different galaxies. On the basis of these images alone, what would you expect the Hubble types of the three galaxies to be?

SAQ 2.3 (Objective 2.2)   Why does the fact that elliptical galaxies have elliptical outlines imply that their stars occupy an ellipsoidal volume of space?

SAQ 2.4 (Objectives 2.2 and 2.3)   Fill in the missing data in Table 2.1, which compares and contrasts various properties of three of the main classes of galaxy. Look at the answer and make sure that you have completed the table correctly, for future reference.

Table 2.1 A comparison of Hubble classes, for SAQ 2.4

Property	Ellipticals	Spirals	Irregulars
approximate proportion of all galaxies	$\geq 60\%$	$\leq 30\%$	$\leq 15\%$
proportion by mass of gas to stars	$\sim 1\%$	5–15%	$15-25\%$
stellar populations	Population II	Population I + II	populations I and II
approximate mass range	$\sim 10^5 - 10^{13} M_\odot$	$\sim 10^9 - 10^{12} M_\odot$	10^9 to $10^{10} M_\odot$
approximate luminosity range	a few times $10^5 L_\odot$ to about $10^{11} L_\odot$	about $10^9 L_\odot$ to a few times $10^{11} L_\odot$	roughly $10^7 L_\odot$ to $10^{10} L_\odot$
approximate diameter range ^{a}	$(0.01–5)\, d_{MW}$	$(0.02–1.5)\, d_{MW}$	$(0.05–0.25)\, d_{MW}$
angular momentum per unit mass	low	high	low

^{a} d_{MW} = diameter of Milky Way.

2.3 The determination of the distances of galaxies

2.3.1 Motives and methods – an introduction

Measuring the distances to external galaxies is a task of crucial importance in modern astronomy. There are three main reasons for this. First, if we want to determine properties of galaxies we often need to know their actual, rather than their apparent, sizes. If the distance d to a galaxy is known, then its angular size θ can be used in the formula $l = d \times (\theta/\text{radians})$ to find the actual size (provided θ is small, which in practice it always will be). Second, galactic distances are crucial to mapping the layout of the Universe. It is easy to identify the directions of observable galaxies and clusters, but only when we also know their distances can we have a full knowledge of how they are arranged in space. The third reason is that galactic distances hold the key to working out the age, evolution and ultimate fate of the Universe, including whether or not it will last for ever – more will be said about these issues in Book 4. For the present it is sufficient to note that scientists are currently working on a number of different theoretical models of the Universe, and. if galactic distances can be measured with sufficient accuracy then it may be possible to discount some of them.

So, the measurement of galactic distances is of great importance. But how is it done, and how reliable are the results? There are many methods of measuring galactic distances and new ones are being developed, or old ones revised and improved, all the time. We cannot hope to give an exhaustive account of this vast subject here, but will deal with the general principles, and then examine a few methods in more detail, noting some of the limitations and shortcomings. The general principles are outlined here, and in later subsections of this chapter we will examine some methods in more detail. Many of the methods for finding distances fall into a few broad categories.

You have already met one geometrical method for determining distances – trigonometric parallax (Book 1, Subsection 2.2.2). This is currently only feasible for objects within the Milky Way; even recent measurements by the Hipparcos satellite (Book 1, Subsection 2.2.2) have extended the range to only about 500 pc.

The basic idea behind the geometrical method used for other galaxies is very simple; within an external galaxy, identify a feature of known linear diameter l, measure the angular diameter, θ, of that feature, then work out the distance, d, of that feature by using the formula $d = l/(\theta/\text{radians})$. (This is just a rearrangement of the formula $l = d(\theta/\text{radians})$ that was quoted earlier in this subsection.) The main shortcoming of this method is equally simple; there are few features of 'known linear diameter' in external galaxies, and even those features that do exist are unlikely to have accurately measurable angular diameters in any external galaxies apart from those that are *very* close to the Milky Way. Despite this severe limitation, one method belonging to this category has recently been used to make what is thought to be an accurate determination of the distance of the nearest external galaxy – the **Large Magellanic Cloud**. The LMC, as it is usually known, was the site of a supernova observed in February 1987 (this is shown in Plate 1.28). Radiation from this event encountered a ring of gas surrounding the supernova and caused it to brighten (see Plate 1.28b). The ring had been blown off by the supernova progenitor, thousands of years before, and has been expanding ever since. Observing from Earth, different parts of the ring appeared to brighten at different times, the delay in the brightening of some parts being due to their greater distance from us and the finite speed of light. Using these delays together with the observed orientation of the ring, and assuming it was circular, it was possible to work out its linear diameter. Comparing this with its angular diameter, the distance of the ring and hence of the LMC itself has been shown to be 52 kpc. This result places the LMC just beyond the outskirts of the Milky Way, in good agreement with independent determinations of its distance by other methods.

ITQ 2.2 Suppose that the ring of gas surrounding the supernova was inclined at 43° from being face-on to our line of sight, and that light from the far side of the ring took 340 days longer to get to us than light from the near side. What would be the diameter of the ring?

Methods involving a 'standard candle'

This category covers a wider range of methods and is much more important than the previous category, but the basic idea is just as simple. A **standard candle** is an object of known luminosity embedded in the object whose distance you want to know. Once a standard candle has been identified, its distance is found by comparing the flux density, F, that it provides to observers on Earth, with its (known) luminosity L. You should already be familiar with this use of flux density since it was used to evaluate stellar distances in Subsection 2.3.4 of Book 1.

ITQ 2.3 On the basis of what you learned in Book 1, and subsequently:
(a) For a 'standard candle' of luminosity L, delivering a flux density F to observers on the surface of the Earth, write down a formula that provides an upper limit for the distance, d, of the galaxy containing the 'candle'.

(b) Explain why the formula you have written down only represents an upper limit on d (as opposed to an accurate value).

Standard candle methods are widely used, and there are many types of object that have been suggested as standard candles. The selection of these objects is of crucial importance, and will be discussed in more detail in Subsection 2.3.3.

Methods involving properties of entire galaxies

There are a number of distance determination methods that rely on the measurement of one or more galactic properties. There is a mixed bag of methods that fall into this broad category, and these are the subject of Subsection 2.3.4. Some of these methods are essentially extensions of the standard candle method since they are based on the identification of a galactic property that is correlated with the luminosity of the galaxy. Others involve properties that do not involve luminosity. The most important of these is based on Hubble's law, a correlation between the distance of a remote galaxy and the redshift of its spectrum. This method is the subject of Subsection 2.3.5.

2.3.2 The galactic distance ladder and its calibration

A major problem is that no single method spans the entire range of distances. Figure 2.9 lists some of the methods of measuring astronomical distances that are the subject of this Course, and indicates the range of distances over which they have been used. (Note that the distance scale is logarithmic, and that the listing includes one method that is confined to the Milky Way.) Almost all methods of distance determination involve using distances found by one method to support another. (You have met this idea before; in Book 1, Subsection 2.2.2, the measurement of stellar distances by trigonometric parallax relies on a knowledge of the Earth's orbital radius, which is itself deduced from other measurements.) The use of a chain of measurements, each relying on another, leads to the so-called **galactic distance ladder** – a ladder in the sense that the accessibility of the upper steps depends on having appropriate steps, firmly in place, lower down.

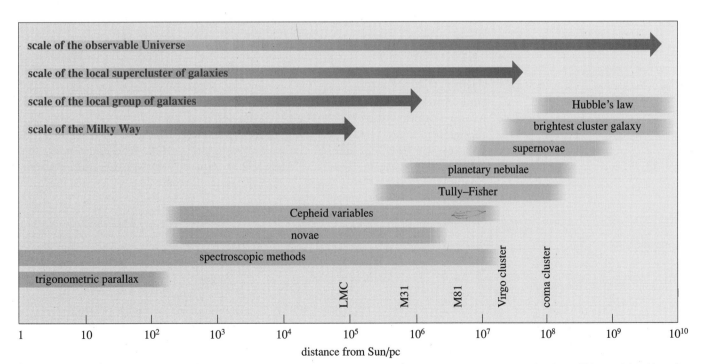

Figure 2.9 Some methods of measuring astronomical distances. Also included are various terms and size scales that will be explained later in this book.

Relating one step on the distance ladder to another requires a process of *calibration*. In principle, this could be achieved using a reliable direct method to measure the absolute distances of some galaxies (suitable methods would be either a geometric method or using a standard candle whose luminosity was firmly established). Direct measurements could then be checked against the distances to the same galaxies found by indirect means, and the indirect methods refined and calibrated accordingly. Unfortunately there is a **calibration problem**: while there are some methods that give *relative* distances reliably, there are very few ways of calibrating indirect methods accurately to get *absolute* distances. So the galactic distance ladder suffers from one great drawback. Just as a ladder with a slight wobble in the lower section will be very shaky further up, so any uncertainties introduced at the bottom of the galactic distance ladder will accumulate to give large uncertainties at the top. As a consequence of the calibration problem and the accumulation of uncertainties over several steps, distances of the most remote galaxies are uncertain by a factor of 2 or so!

The next three subsections examine some of the methods of distance determination in more detail. Subsection 2.3.3 deals with some of the standard candle methods and Subsection 2.3.4 with a variety of methods that use the properties of entire galaxies. Subsection 2.3.5 deals with the crucially important topic of Hubble's law.

2.3.3 Standard candles – first steps on the ladder

Standard candle methods have played an important role in the history of galactic distance determinations and have great potential for the future. This subsection considers three representatives of this class of methods in more detail, concentrating in each case on the two fundamental problems that face every standard candle technique.

- Which astronomical sources are suitable to be standard candles?
- What is the luminosity of a selected standard candle?

The Cepheid variable method

As described in Subsections 2.4.2 and 3.4.3 of Book 1, Cepheids are giant or supergiant stars with a variable light output that can change by as much as a factor of ten over a period that may be anything from about a day to about 100 days. A **light curve** showing the variation of apparent visual magnitude V with time for one particular Cepheid is given in Figure 2.10. Cepheids have quite high average luminosities so they are visible even at quite large distances. The recognition that a class of such highly individual stars could be used as standard candles was the outcome of the collective efforts of three astronomers, the American Henrietta Leavitt (1868–1921), Ejnar Hertzsprung and Harlow Shapley.

Book 1, Subsection 2.3.4, outlined the magnitude system of measuring brightness.

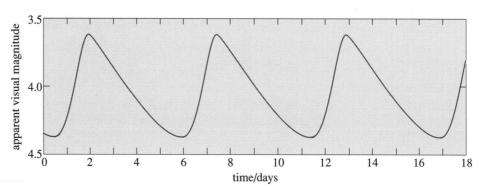

Figure 2.10 The light curve of the Cepheid variable δ Cephei.

In 1907, while examining variables in the **Small Magellanic Cloud** (SMC) (a very nearby galaxy), Leavitt discovered a correlation between the period of a certain kind of variable star and its maximum apparent magnitude. Since all the stars in the SMC are at roughly the same distance from the Sun, it followed from Leavitt's discovery that there must also be a correlation between the periods of such variables and their luminosities. This implicit **period–luminosity relationship** presented the possibility that the luminosity of any of Leavitt's variables might be deduced from its period of variation. It was first necessary to *calibrate* the period–luminosity relationship by measuring the luminosity of at least one variable star of the appropriate type. This was Hertzsprung's particular contribution – and it was no easy matter.

Hertzsprung's first achievement was recognizing that Leavitt's variables were in fact Cepheids. This insight reduced the calibration problem to that of measuring the luminosity of a Cepheid, but the task was still not simple. (There were many known Cepheids within the Milky Way, but none of them close enough for its distance to be determined by the method of trigonometric parallax (Book 1, Subsection 2.2.2), and thus their luminosities could not be determined.) So, Hertzsprung was forced to use more complicated and less reliable methods in order to obtain the luminosity of a Cepheid. This he eventually did, though for various reasons, including a serious underestimate of the effects of interstellar absorption, his calibration was inaccurate and the value for the distance of the Small Magellanic Cloud quite wrong.

Modern versions of the Cepheid period–luminosity relationship have, of course, been recalibrated, though there is still some debate about the accuracy. A recent version of the relation is shown in Figure 2.11. Two points should be noted. First, despite its name, the period–luminosity relationship is usually presented as a relationship between period and maximum absolute magnitude (i.e. the peak magnitude an object would have if viewed from a distance of 10 pc; see Book 1, Subsection 2.3.4). Secondly, the magnitude used is usually restricted to one or other of the standard wavelength bands used by astronomers, such as the V (visual) band introduced in Subsection 2.3.4 of Book 1.

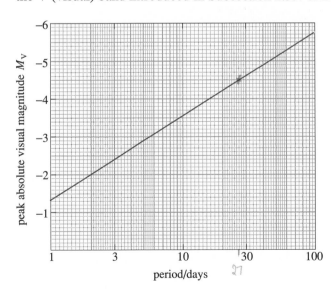

Figure 2.11 The period–luminosity relationship for Cepheid variables. Note that, in accordance with convention, the luminosity is actually represented by peak absolute magnitude (rather than mean luminosity). (The data here are for type I (classical) Cepheids. Type II Cepheids have lower luminosity than type I of comparable period.)

ITQ 2.4 A certain Cepheid is observed to have a period of 10 days. What is the maximum absolute visual magnitude of the Cepheid expected to be?

The **Cepheid variable method** has played an important part in the history of astronomical distance measurements. It was employed, somewhat erroneously, by Harlow Shapley who developed his own independent version of the method during his studies of the distribution of globular clusters, and it was used by Hubble to determine the distance of the spiral galaxy M31 (see Plate 3.8b). It was this latter measurement, announced in 1924, that convinced the majority of astronomers that there were galaxies external to the Milky Way and thus ushered in the era of galactic astronomy. Figure 2.12 shows the photographic plate that Hubble was studying when he realized that what he had thought was a *nova* was in fact a Cepheid that held the key to M31's distance.

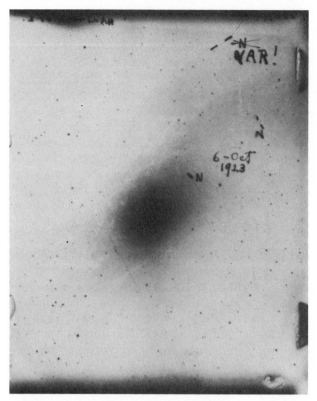

Figure 2.12 The photographic plate of M31 on which Hubble discovered a Cepheid. Note that the N (for nova) at the top right has been crossed out and VAR (for variable) written in its place.

1 Mpc (megaparsec) = 10^6 pc = 10^3 kpc.

At the time of writing (1994), the Cepheid variable method is still limited to distances of less than about 7.5 Mpc. This is not far in cosmic terms but it is far enough to encompass the whole of the **Local Group** – a sparse association of 30 or so galaxies within about 1 Mpc of the Milky Way. (M31, M33, the LMC, the SMC and the Milky Way are all members of the Local Group.) In fact, the Cepheid variable method is the source of the most accurate distance measurements currently available for many of the galaxies in the Local Group. With the advent of the Hipparcos satellite and a number of large, new, ground-based telescopes (such as those featured in TV programme 2), it is expected that the range and accuracy of the method will undergo further improvements over the next few years. If so, it may even be able to provide a reliable estimate of the distance to the **Virgo cluster** – the nearest rich cluster of galaxies. In the Virgo cluster more than 2000 galaxies are packed into a volume not much bigger than that occupied by the 30 or so of the Local Group. It is currently thought that the Virgo cluster is between 15 and 25 Mpc from the Milky Way. An accurate determination of its distance might well hold the key to the measurement of very much greater distances.

It is also worth noting that, although the period–luminosity relationship was discovered empirically, there seems to be a good underlying physical explanation for it. The variation in luminosity of a Cepheid is thought to arise because the entire star is pulsating (i.e. expanding and contracting regularly), with the period of the pulsations depending on the mass of the star. The more massive the star, the larger and hotter (and thus more luminous) it will be, hence there will be a relation between period and luminosity.

Supernova methods

Figure 2.13 shows a supernova in an external galaxy. As you can see the supernova is very bright compared with the rest of its host galaxy and is easily discerned. Supernovae are classified as Type I or II mainly on the basis of their light curves and spectra (Book 1, Chapter 4). Members of a subclass of Type I, **Type Ia supernovae** are the brightest and, fortunately, the most homogeneous class of supernovae. Over the past 30 years or so, three galaxies have each been observed to host two Type Ia supernovae and in each of these three galaxies the two supernovae have had almost the same maximum apparent brightness, suggesting that Type Ia supernovae might be standard candles. There is also a good *physical* reason to suppose that Type Ia supernovae should be standard candles. As described in Book 1, Chapter 4, it is thought that at least some Type I supernovae are produced in binary stars in which one of the pair has evolved to become a white dwarf or neutron star while its less massive partner is at an earlier stage of development. When the less massive star evolves and overflows its Roche lobe, matter is transferred to its companion, triggering a violent explosion when the companion reaches a critical mass. If indeed Type Ia supernovae are all produced by similar types of companion star reaching the same critical mass, it is reasonable to suppose that they should all have similar luminosities.

Figure 2.13 The nearby galaxy NGC 5253 (a) before (1959) and (b) during the eruption of the type Ia supernova 1972E. The supernova itself is the bright dot to the lower right of the galaxy image in (b).

Having identified Type Ia supernovae as possible standard candles, the next requirement is calibration – the luminosity of a typical Type Ia must be determined from direct observation or by reliable calculation. The theoretical understanding of Type Ia supernovae has improved enormously over just the past few years, but it is still not good enough to be the sole means of calibration. Fortunately, there are observations that can contribute to the calibration process.

ITQ 2.5   Three Type Ia supernovae have been observed in nearby galaxies. List the items of information concerning these supernovae and their host galaxies that you would need in order to calibrate the Type Ia supernova method. Briefly explain how you would use the items in your list.

Studies of the sort outlined in the answer to ITQ 2.5 indicate that the peak luminosity of a typical Type Ia supernova is about $5.5 \times 10^9 L_{\odot}$. At one time it seemed that Type Ia supernovae would be accurate standard candles that could be used out to large distances. Unfortunately, Type Ia supernovae observed within the Virgo cluster (and hence at approximately the same distance) show a greater spread in their maximum apparent magnitudes than is desirable, so the reliability of this method has been called into question – even so, it is still used.

Another method has been suggested that uses supernovae of any type and may have fewer problems than the Type Ia method. The method uses the Doppler effect which, as you saw in Book 1, Subsection 2.2.1, relates the shift in frequency of spectral lines to the speed of their source towards or away from the observer. Doppler shifts in spectral lines from a supernova are used to estimate the expansion speed, and hence the size, of the emitting region. The temperature of the region is estimated by observing it at different wavelengths, which together with its size gives an estimate of the luminosity. The distance can then be calculated.

The planetary nebula luminosity function method

Planetary nebulae were discussed in Book 1, Subsections 2.5.2 and 3.4.4; they are gaseous shells found around some hot stars, thought to have been ejected during post-main-sequence evolution. Observations of planetary nebulae in galaxies of known distance indicate that the *brightest* planetary nebulae in each galaxy seem to have similar luminosities, and that this luminosity is independent of the type of galaxy. Figure 2.14 shows a typical **planetary nebula luminosity function** (PNLF) for planetary nebulae in a galaxy, i.e. a plot showing the numbers of planetary nebulae with various luminosities. In all such plots, the graph curves over and meets the horizontal axis at approximately the same luminosity. To apply the method to a galaxy whose distance is unknown, the flux densities of its planetary nebulae are measured and used to plot their *observed* PNLF (using flux density, not luminosity, but it is still called a luminosity function), which is used to deduce the flux density we would receive from the brightest planetary nebulae in that galaxy. The relationship between this flux density and the assumed 'standard' luminosity gives the distance, as in ITQ 2.3.

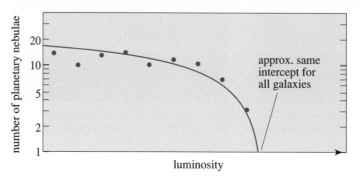

Figure 2.14   The observed PNLF for the galaxy M31.

The calibration of this method is, of course, the measurement of the luminosity of the brightest planetary nebulae in galaxies of known distances – measurements which in turn depend on having found the distances of these galaxies by some other means. The use of planetary nebulae as standard candles differs from the previous two methods in that it is empirical and, as yet, there seems to be no physical explanation for it. It also differs in that it is a statistical method: a single planetary nebula does not on its own constitute a standard candle – a whole collection need to be observed within a galaxy. It does, though, have several advantages over other methods. Planetary nebulae are found in galaxies of all Hubble classes, and are often found in relatively dust-free regions – making observation easy, so the method is becoming increasingly widely used.

ITQ 2.6   What would be some further advantages of using planetary nebulae, rather than Cepheids or supernovae, to determine distances?

2.3.4 Properties of entire galaxies – stepping up the ladder

Methods in this broad category generally extend the scale to greater distances than those discussed above. All rely on calibration using distances found by other methods, and some involve the correlation of galactic luminosity with other properties.

One method that has been applied to over a thousand galaxies makes use of the so-called **Tully–Fisher relation**. This particular relationship, discovered in 1977, links the luminosity of a spiral galaxy to the width of the 21 cm emission line in the galaxy's radio spectrum. (The origin of this line, due to atomic hydrogen, was discussed in Subsection 5.2.1 of Book 1.) The relationship is in accord with the idea that more massive (and, presumably, more luminous) galaxies should be rotating more rapidly (as shown in Chapter 1 of this book, orbital speed depends on the mass enclosed by the orbit) and will therefore contain a greater range of velocites along a line of sight, giving rise to a broader line.

In order to use the relationship to find unknown distances, the relationship needs to be calibrated – in other words, the distances and hence luminosities of some galaxies must have been found by some other method. The Tully–Fisher method must also take into account the orientation of the galaxy relative to the observer and any absorption/scattering that occurs along the light path. Still, 21 cm line widths are relatively easy to measure, so this method has received a good deal of attention in recent years.

Another method is that of **brightest cluster galaxies**. In some regions of space, galaxies are gathered together into groups or **clusters** that vary considerably in size and richness. It appears that, for the richer clusters, the luminosity of the brightest galaxy in each cluster is much the same in all such clusters, so this is essentially another standard candle method. As always, the method requires calibration – the 'standard' luminosity must first be determined for some clusters using distances found by another method. The flux density received from the brightest galaxy in a rich cluster is then used to determine the distance of that cluster (as in ITQ 2.3). Clearly, this method has the potential of probing very deeply into the Universe. Indeed, due to the lack of rich clusters near at hand, it cannot be applied at all to any galaxy within about 20 Mpc.

Establishing Hubble's law

The terms redshift and blueshift should already be familiar to you. Both were introduced in Book 1, Subsection 2.2.1, where you saw that they referred respectively to increases and decreases in the wavelength of identifiable spectral features, such as spectral lines. In the context of Book 1 you saw that one way that such shifts could arise is as a consequence of the Doppler effect and the shifts could therefore be used to measure the speed at which a source of radiation was receding from, or approaching, an observer.

The spectra of galaxies also exhibit redshifts. You will learn later that they are *not* simply the result of the Doppler effect, though they do arise from a change in time of the separation between us and the galaxies. A redshift corresponds to an *increasing* separation. Setting the explanation aside for now, a galactic redshift is shown schematically in Figure 2.15 and exemplified in Plate 3.11. To evaluate redshift z in a specific case, all that is needed is a value for the observed wavelength (λ_{obs}) of a spectral line that has a known wavelength (λ_{em}) at the point of emission. The value of z can then be obtained from the definition of z:

$$z = \frac{\lambda_{obs} - \lambda_{em}}{\lambda_{em}} = \frac{\lambda_{obs}}{\lambda_{em}} - 1 \tag{2.1}$$

Generally speaking, all the spectral lines originating in a distant galaxy will be redshifted to about the same extent, so it is possible to represent the redshift of any particular galaxy by a single number. In practice, things might be a good deal more complicated. It might for instance be necessary to measure several lines to obtain z, but the principle remains the same. In the few cases where a galaxy shows a blueshift rather than a redshift, Equation 2.1 would give a negative value for z. Throughout this chapter we shall speak exclusively of **redshifts**, with the tacit understanding that blueshifts are included as redshifts with negative values of z.

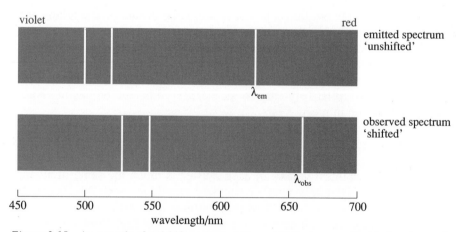

Figure 2.15   As a result of redshift, a spectral line emitted at a wavelength λ_{em} is seen by observers at a wavelength λ_{obs}.

☐   Suppose that one of the 'unshifted' spectral lines had been the line of singly ionized calcium (Ca$^+$) which is emitted at a wavelength of 393.4 nm, and that the 'shifted' wavelength at which this line was observed on Earth was 469.2 nm. What would be the redshift of the galaxy from which the line was emitted?

■ $z = \dfrac{469.2 - 393.4}{393.4} = 0.19$

In the late 1920s, when most astronomical measurements were a good deal harder to perform than they are now, only a few galaxies had their redshifts measured. Nonetheless, as Hubble followed up his determination of the distance to M31 with various other galactic distance determinations, he was able to compare distances with redshifts for a growing sample of galaxies. By 1929, using a sample of just 24 galaxies, he presented the first convincing evidence of a linear relationship between the redshifts and distances of galaxies. In modernized notation, we now write that relationship in the form

$$z = \frac{H_0}{c} d \tag{2.2}$$

where c is the speed of light ($3.00 \times 10^8 \, \text{m s}^{-1}$) and H_0 is a constant known as **Hubble's constant**.

The linear relationship between z and d is not a perfect one, as you can see from Figure 2.16. Nonetheless, Equation 2.2, idealized though it may be, does sum up the general trend of a great deal of data and is one of the standard ways of expressing what is now known as **Hubble's law**. This relationship is interpreted as showing that the Universe as a whole is expanding.

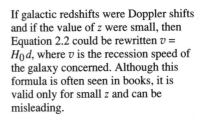

If galactic redshifts were Doppler shifts and if the value of z were small, then Equation 2.2 could be rewritten $v = H_0 d$, where v is the recession speed of the galaxy concerned. Although this formula is often seen in books, it is valid only for small z and can be misleading.

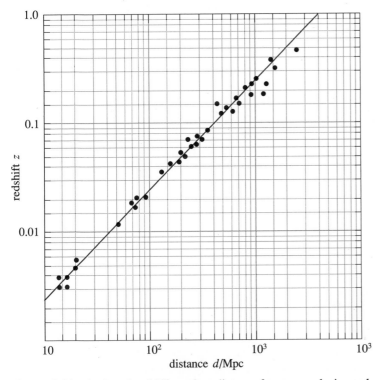

Figure 2.16 A plot of redshift against distance for some galaxies and clusters of galaxies. Note that there is a some scatter about the straight line. (The value of H_0 here is $75 \, \text{km s}^{-1} \, \text{Mpc}^{-1}$ – see overleaf.)

Using Hubble's law

Clearly, despite some deviations from the linear relationship, Hubble's law has great potential as a method of determining the distances of galaxies. Now that redshifts can be measured with relative ease, it would appear to be a simple matter to determine the distance of any galaxy if we know the value of Hubble's constant H_0. Evaluating H_0 is, of course, nothing other than the *calibration problem* for this method of determining distances. The determination of Hubble's constant has been one of the major problems in astronomy since the discovery of Hubble's law.

☐ In what units would you express H_0 if you knew its value?

■ z is a ratio of similar quantities, so it has no units. Thus, H_0 should have the same units as c/d. If we use SI units, then c is measured in $m\,s^{-1}$ and d in m, with the consequence that H_0 is measured in s^{-1}. However, since astronomers mainly measure extragalactic distances in Mpc a reasonable alternative is to express H_0 in $m\,s^{-1}\,Mpc^{-1}$.

You may therefore be justifiably surprised to learn that astronomers conventionally express H_0 in terms of $km\,s^{-1}\,Mpc^{-1}$.

Different investigators favour different ends of this range.

Current estimates of Hubble's constant put it roughly in the range 50–100 $km\,s^{-1}\,Mpc^{-1}$, and in this Course we will use 75 $km\,s^{-1}\,Mpc^{-1}$ as a working value. The uncertainty over the value, despite herculean efforts to determine it precisely, is an indication of the difficulty of calibrating the method. At the lower end of the galactic distance scale, where distances and redshifts are reasonably well determined, the high degree of scatter (evident in Figure 2.16) prevents accurate calibration. It might be thought that this difficulty could be overcome simply by using a different sample of galaxies extending out to much greater redshifts. This is indeed true in principle, but in practice the more remote galaxies with larger redshifts are at distances which have themselves only been determined with poor accuracy. Thus, the calibration problem remains insurmountable in the absence of more accurate distance determinations for a sample of far-off galaxies.

Despite the uncertainty over the precise value of Hubble's constant there can be no doubting the importance of Hubble's law. For many purposes, an uncertainty by a factor of 2 in the distances of remote galaxies is of little consequence, especially when Hubble's law continues to provide a clear guide to the *relative* distances of those galaxies (i.e. it still enables us to say that one is, say, twice as far away as another, even if we are not sure of the exact distance to either). Indeed in recent years a number of redshift surveys have been carried out, involving the measurement of thousands of galactic redshifts, with the explicit aim of determining, at least approximately, the *relative* locations of those galaxies and thus elucidating the three-dimensional distribution of galaxies over very large regions of the Universe (see Chapter 4).

Summary of Section 2.3 and SAQs

1 Determining the distances of galaxies is of great importance in astronomy. Distance information can be crucial to the determination of other galactic properties; it plays a vital part in investigations of the large-scale distribution of galaxies; and it may provide the key to understanding the nature of the Universe as a whole.

2 There are many different methods of distance determination. Those applicable to galaxies include: geometrical methods, such as those based on the diameters of material illuminated by supernovae; standard candle methods, such as those based on Cepheid variables, Type Ia supernovae or PNLFs; and methods involving galactic properties such as the width of 21 cm emission lines (the Tully–Fisher relation), the apparent magnitude of brightest cluster galaxies, and the galactic redshift.

3 The various methods, taken together, form a galactic distance ladder in which the calibration process, that most steps require, is usually dependent on the accuracy of other steps lower down the ladder. This means that uncertainties tend to increase as the ladder is climbed.

4   The distances of the most remote galaxies may be determined using Hubble's law, which relates distance to redshift. However, the difficulty of calibrating the method (i.e. the difficulty of determining Hubble's constant) means that such distances are currently uncertain to within a factor of two.

SAQ 2.5 (Objective 2.5)   What is (a) the period and (b) the peak absolute visual magnitude M_V of δ Cephei, the subject of Figure 2.10?

SAQ 2.6 (Objective 2.5)   List some of the shortcomings of standard candle methods for finding distances.

SAQ 2.7 (Objectives 2.5 and 2.6)   (a) How might the data points at the larger distances on the horizontal axis of Figure 2.16, that correspond to *clusters* of galaxies, have been obtained?

(b) The points in Figure 2.16 for z up to ~0.1 define a reasonably precise straight line. Why cannot the value of H_0 obtained from this plot be relied upon as the *precise* value of Hubble's constant?

2.4   The determination of the properties of galaxies

In Section 2.2 various assertions were made about the physical characteristics of the different types of galaxy included in the Hubble classification. Much of this information was given in Table 2.1 which indicated typical ranges for quantities such as luminosity, diameter, mass and stellar content, without making any serious attempt to explain how such information was obtained. This section is concerned with just such determinations.

2.4.1   Luminosities and sizes of galaxies

Photographed through a sufficiently powerful telescope, most galaxies are seen as faint, extended objects with a brightness that varies from point to point. In studying the energy received from such objects the quantity that is directly measured is the **apparent surface brightness** of the source. This quantity can be roughly thought of as the flux reaching $1\,m^2$ (i.e. the flux density) from a small region of angular area $1\,arcsec^2$ surrounding the point being observed (see Figure 2.17). Thus the units of apparent surface brightness are $W\,m^{-2}\,arcsec^{-2}$.

    The extended nature of galactic images is a source of difficulty for those engaged in measuring galactic luminosities – it is much easier to deal with point sources like stars. Galaxies do not have sharp edges – they just fade out so it is hard to know where to stop measuring. To overcome this problem, measurements are often restricted to the relatively brighter parts of a galaxy, usually within an **isophote**; that is, a closed curve connecting points of constant apparent surface brightness, in much the same way that a hill is enclosed by a height contour. Given the type of galaxy being observed and the flux density we receive from within the selected isophote, the total flux density we receive can then be estimated on the basis of certain standard brightness profiles that have been obtained observationally (see Figure 2.18).

    Once the total flux density that we receive has been measured, other corrections can be applied. For example, in the case of spiral galaxies, the orientation relative to the observer (see Figure 2.19) can be estimated from the observed ratio of major to minor axes in the observed galaxy (within the selected isophote). Standard corrections arising from the orientation itself and its influence on absorption within the observed galaxy can then be applied. The

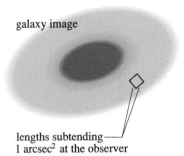

galaxy image

lengths subtending 1 arcsec² at the observer

Figure 2.17   The apparent surface brightness of a galaxy provides a measure of the flux density originating in an angular area of 1 arcsec² surrounding the point being observed.

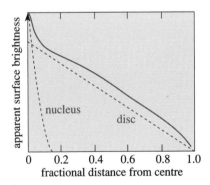

Figure 2.18   Apparent surface brightness as a function of fractional distance from the galactic centre for an averaged sample of face-on Sc galaxies. The dashed lines show the contributions from the nuclear bulge and from a smooth disc (as in an S0 galaxy). The solid line includes both contributions together with the contribution from the spiral arms that augment the light output of the disc.

The luminosity is given by $L = 4\pi d^2 F$ (see ITQ 2.5), and the linear diameter by $l = d \times (\theta/\text{radians})$ (see Subsection 2.3.1).

'corrected' flux density F that emerges from such a calculation together with the distance d of the galaxy will then provide a value for the luminosity L of the galaxy, after making due allowance for interstellar absorption within the Milky Way. Similarly, the angular diameter within a selected isophote can be used to estimate the angular diameter θ of the whole galaxy, which can in turn be used in conjunction with the distance of the galaxy to determine its linear diameter l. These procedures are subject to many uncertainties and assumptions so cannot possibly provide an absolutely precise value of any physical quantity. Rather, the aim is to approach the determination in a standardized way, so that comparisons between the luminosities and diameters of different galaxies are as meaningful as possible.

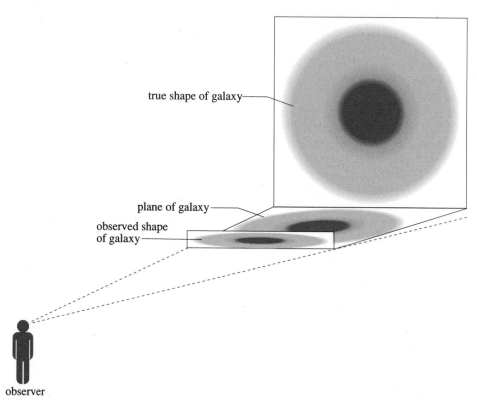

true shape of galaxy

plane of galaxy

observed shape of galaxy

observer

Figure 2.19   The observed shape of a galaxy arises from a combination of its true shape and its orientation relative to the observer.

The results of luminosity and diameter determinations have already been summarized in Table 2.1. Basically, ellipticals are the most diverse class with luminosities that range from a few times $10^5 L_\odot$ for dwarf elliptical galaxies to about $10^{11} L_\odot$ for giant cD galaxies, such as M87 in the Virgo cluster (Plate 3.21). Spirals, on the other hand, occupy a narrower range, from about 10^9 to a few times $10^{11} L_\odot$. Irregulars occupy a wider range than spirals, but are generally less luminous. Diameters follow a similar pattern, as Table 2.1 shows.

2.4.2   Masses of galaxies

You will recall from Chapter 1 that a great deal of uncertainty still surrounds the mass of the Milky Way – mainly due to the problem of assessing how much **dark matter** is associated with our Galaxy. Similar problems are associated with all galaxies. Thus, although four methods of determining galactic masses will be briefly described you should not be surprised to learn that the results they provide are not fully consistent since they certainly differ in their sensitivity to dark matter and may also have other shortcomings.

The use of a **rotation curve** – a plot of circular orbital speed, v, against radial distance from the galactic centre – to determine the mass of a spiral galaxy has already been described in Subsection 1.2.5. The basic principles are quite simple; the rotation curve of a galaxy is measured observationally and compared with the theoretical rotation curve predicted by a model of the galaxy in which mass (including dark matter) is distributed in a plausible way, including that in the halo. The theoretical mass distribution is then adjusted until there is reasonable agreement between the observed curve and the predicted curve. The total mass in the final model (including dark matter) then represents the true mass of the galaxy. The method suffers from various drawbacks, including the fact that (owing to assumptions about symmetry on which the method relies) it is rather unsuitable for spirals that have strongly pronounced bars, and the fact that it gives only a lower limit to the galactic mass. The method also depends on knowing the radial distance r, which in turn requires that the distance of the galaxy is known. Nonetheless, it is relatively straightforward and has been used extensively.

ITQ 2.7 Why does the method only give a lower limit on the mass? (This limitation was discussed in Chapter 1.)

In order to ensure that observations of rotation curves extend out to the greatest possible values of r, it is usual to base them on Doppler shifts of the 21 cm line. This is the subject of video sequence 10. In external galaxies the detectable 21 cm emission from neutral hydrogen can often be traced well beyond the optical limits of the disc (remember that dark matter would extend still further). Some rotation curves obtained in this way are shown in Figure 2.20. For nearby galaxies, the rotation curve can be obtained from 21 cm Doppler shifts measured at several different points in the galaxy, as shown in a colour-coded form in Plate 3.12. To derive the rotation curve from the line of sight velocity components shown in the plate it is necessary to take into account the orientation of the galaxy relative to the observer. For more distant galaxies, the rotation curve can be deduced from the width of the 21 cm spectral line, as this depends on the range of velocities present along the line of sight.

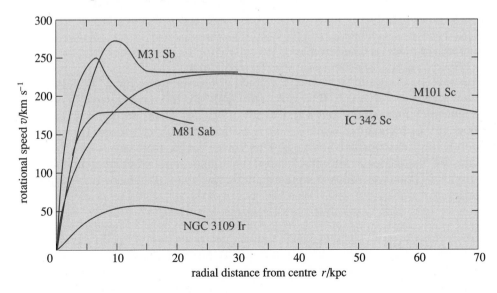

Figure 2.20 Schematic representations of the rotation curves for some nearby galaxies. Note that each curve is marked with the catalogue designation and Hubble type of the galaxy to which it refers.

Irrespective of their limitations, 21 cm measurements of rotation curves and the related mass determinations have been of great significance in modern astronomy. The evidence they have provided of galactic mass distributions that extend well beyond the limits of visible discs has played an important part in giving dark matter its current significance.

As mentioned above, video sequence 10 A radio astronomy project *is about 21 cm line emission and rotation curves, so now would be a good point at which to view it and work through the associated project.*

Method 2: Velocity dispersions for elliptical galaxies

Rotation (an orderly motion in one plane around the galactic centre) is relatively unimportant in elliptical galaxies, which are often regarded as simple 'star piles' – swarms of stars that have long since settled down into galactic orbits under one another's gravitational influence. If this view of generally settled stellar motions within an elliptical galaxy is correct, then it should be possible to predict the value of a quantity called the **velocity dispersion**, σ, for a given elliptical galaxy. The velocity dispersion is a statistical quantity that can be used to help characterize the behaviour of a group of stars. Roughly speaking, it provides a measure of the range of speeds of stars along a line of sight. The velocity dispersion in an elliptical galaxy of given shape is expected to be proportional to the quantity $(M/R)^{\frac{1}{2}}$, where M is the mass of the galaxy and R is a scale length related to its radius. This result, derived from what is known as the **virial theorem**, may be applied to elliptical galaxies whose size R is known and for which σ can be estimated from redshift measurements. This procedure seems to give reasonable values for M, though, once again, the mass obtained is only a lower limit since it is really that enclosed by the stellar orbits. Note that the virial theorem applies only to a system of objects moving in *random* orbits while bound by each other's gravity – the generally well-ordered motion within spiral galaxies means that their masses cannot be estimated in this way.

This derivation is beyond the scope of S281.

Method 3: X-ray halos of ellipticals

Some bright ellipticals have substantial halos of hot diffuse gas with temperatures of several million kelvins. The temperature and density of the gas can be determined from its X-ray spectrum, and hence its mass can be deduced. This method is becoming widely used, and provides evidence for substantial amounts of material (mainly hydrogen) occupying larger volumes than the matter in elliptical galaxies that emits at visible wavelengths.

Method 4: Binary galaxies

There are a number of cases in which one galaxy is found in close physical association with another, and it seems reasonable to assume that the two galaxies are orbiting each other. Such gravitationally bound pairs are called **binary galaxies** by analogy with the binary stars that were introduced in Book 1, Chapter 2. Binary galaxies can provide information about galactic masses just as binary stars can give insight into stellar masses (Book 1, Subsection 2.5.1). In the galactic case complete orbits require immense amounts of time (of order 10^{10} years) and hence cannot be observed, but other data, such as Doppler shifts, can yield information about the orbital motions of the galaxies. Owing to uncertainties about the orientation of the orbit, it is not possible to deduce the mass of any individual galaxy from observations of binary pairs, but the method can be applied to a sample of similar pairs, on a statistical basis, in the hope that the orbits are randomly orientated. The result of averaging measurements over many similar pairs of galaxies yields an estimate of the typical total mass of one such pair, which can then be halved to give an estimate of the mass of a single galaxy.

The method has been applied to pairs of similar Hubble type with the result that average masses of $3 \times 10^{10} M_\odot$ are found for Sc and irregular galaxies, $6 \times 10^{10} M_\odot$ for Sa and Sb galaxies, and $6 \times 10^{11} M_\odot$ for elliptical and lenticular galaxies. The advantage of this method is that it should reflect the (average) total mass of each type and not just the mass of the visible parts. However, there are also many difficulties and disadvantages. The main problem is the statistical nature of the method. It has proved very difficult to identify sufficiently large samples that are certain to be true binaries. Moreover, the results are sensitive to the way in which matter is distributed in the galaxies under scrutiny – currently a highly contentious issue. Consequently, it would be inappropriate to put great reliance upon the results of this particular method.

Method 5: Galaxies in clusters

This method is essentially the same as method 2. Just as the velocity dispersion, σ, of stars in an elliptical galaxy can be related to the mass of that galaxy, so the velocity dispersion of galaxies within a cluster can be related to the mass of that cluster using the result of the virial theorem. The masses of clusters are generally found to be of the order ten times greater than the sum of the masses of the matter that has been detected via radiation, and this is evidence for substantial amounts of dark matter in clusters. We shall return to this result in Chapter 4 and in Book 4.

2.4.3 Compositions of galaxies

The answer to the question 'What are galaxies made of?' should already be familiar to you. Broadly speaking, galaxies are made of dark matter, stars, and ordinary (baryonic) gas together with various minor constituents (such as dust and cosmic rays). This subsection is concerned with the methods employed to determine the detailed compositions of individual galaxies. It aims to explain how we set about answering questions such as: 'How many stars are there in a galaxy?' or 'What kind of stars predominate?' or 'How much of the galaxy's mass is in the form of ordinary gas (baryonic, non-dark, matter)?'

The last of the above questions is one of the simplest to answer. At least, there is a relatively straightforward procedure for attaching a numerical value to the quantity M_H/M, where M_H is the mass of atomic hydrogen in a galaxy and M is the 'total' mass of that galaxy estimated from its rotation curve or velocity dispersion. The determination of M_H can be simply based on the flux density of 21 cm radiation received from atomic hydrogen in the galaxy, though whereas in some cases atomic hydrogen may be the dominant form of hydrogen in a galaxy, there is evidence that certain galaxies are dominated by H_2. Studies of the ratio M_H/M indicate a fairly systematic variation with Hubble type. Ellipticals have very little baryonic gas, spirals a few per cent and irregulars 15–25%.

Questions about the numbers and types of stars in a galaxy are really interconnected and are best answered together. In principle a galaxy might be expected to contain representatives of all the stellar types that were discussed in Book 1. However, in view of the relative amounts of gas in the various classes of galaxy, it is only reasonable to suppose that star formation, which requires gas, will be rare in ellipticals and common in irregulars. It is thus reasonable to suppose that those types of stars that belong to population I will be exceptional in elliptical galaxies, but to what extent do observations support that idea? The absence of bright star-forming regions in elliptical galaxies is easily confirmed by direct observation, but such observations are not able to provide an accurate picture of the relative abundances of the various stellar types since only the brightest sorts of stars are visible individually in even the nearest galaxies.

Another technique is needed to investigate stellar contents, one that can be based on the properties of a galaxy treated as a whole.

The main method used to investigate the stellar contents of galaxies is known as **population synthesis.** It may make use of a variety of galactic properties including the mass M, luminosity L, and the **mass to light ratio** M/L, but its major ingredient is the overall spectrum of the entire galaxy or at least some large region of the galaxy – the so-called **integrated spectrum.** A major problem of stellar population synthesis is that cool low-mass stars that contribute much of the total mass do not emit much visible light, so it is best to include infrared, as well as visual, observations. An example of an integrated spectrum, that for the bar of the Large Magellanic Cloud (Plate 3.10b), is shown in Figure 2.21; some of its features will be due to gas but many will result from the combined spectra of the stars in the region under examination. The method of population synthesis starts by defining a number of different stellar categories. A plausible assumption is made about the relative abundance of the stars in each category and on this basis their contribution to the total mass and luminosity of the galaxy can be worked out. It is also possible to work out the integrated stellar spectrum that would be expected from such a combination of stars. The results of these various calculations are then compared with the observed spectrum and the mix of stars adjusted to improve the agreement. The result of one attempt at population synthesis for the nuclear bulge of M31 (Plate 3.8b) is shown in Table 2.2.

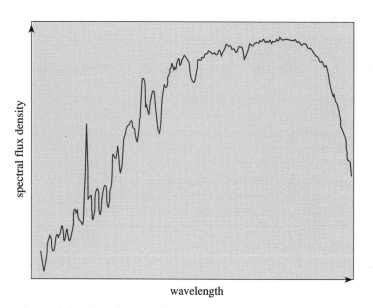

Figure 2.21 The integrated spectrum of the bar of the Large Magellanic Cloud. (No scales were given by the authors of the research paper from which this figure is adapted.)

Once a population model has been formulated, the known luminosity of each kind of star can be used in conjunction with the total luminosity of the galaxy to find the total number of stars in the galaxy. The relative importance of the various minor constituents can usually be deduced from observations made at a variety of wavelengths: infrared observations help to determine the dust content, while radio observations indicate the significance of cosmic rays and magnetic fields.

Table 2.2 An example of a population model of M31's nuclear bulge. The letters SMR stand for 'super-metal-rich' and refer to a particular compositional feature.

Stellar category	Contribution to total mass/%	Contribution to (V band) luminosity/%
Main sequence:		
G0–G4	0.77	11.56
G5–K0	0.76	3.10
K1–K2	0.40	2.29
K3–K4	0.78	3.07
K5–K7	1.12	1.24
M0–M2	0.73	0.27
M3–M4	10.3	1.09
M5–M6	4.6	0.15
M7	69.4	1.74
Subgiants:		
G0–G4	0.35	11.88
G5–G9	0.26	8.79
K0–K1 (SMR)	0.13	6.74
K2 (SMR) [a]	0.12	26.57
Giants:		
K3 (SMR)	0.03	12.23
K4–K5 (SMR)	0.01	5.98
M5–M6 (SMR)	0.003	1.32

[a] Includes K2 (SMR) giants too.

Summary of Section 2.4 and SAQs

1   The surface brightness of galaxies varies from point to point. Continuous lines passing through points of equal surface brightness are called isophotes. As it is often difficult to determine the edge of a galaxy, observations of galaxies are often confined to the region within some specified isophotal contour.

2   Empirical relations obtained from observations of nearby galaxies are used to estimate quantities such as the luminosity and angular size of a distant galaxy on the basis of its flux within a given isophotal contour.

3   Galactic masses are generally hard to measure. However, the methods that may be used to determine them include the use of rotation curves for spirals, and velocity dispersions and X-ray halos for ellipticals, together with binary galaxy techniques for binary galaxies, and velocity dispersions for clusters of galaxies.

4   The masses of clusters of galaxies are of the order ten times greater than the estimated masses of the matter that has been detected via electromagnetic radiation, indicating that they contain substantial amounts of dark matter.

5   The stellar content of galaxies can be estimated through the process of population synthesis. Direct observations at various wavelengths can be used to establish the importance of atomic hydrogen, dust, cosmic rays and various other constituents within a galaxy.

SAQ 2.8 (Objective 2.8)   Sketch some typical isophotal contours of (a) an E4 galaxy and (b) a face-on S0 galaxy.

SAQ 2.9 (Objective 2.9)   Why is it not possible to use the rotation curve method to determine the masses of elliptical galaxies, or the virial theorem method to find the masses of spirals?

SAQ 2.10 (Objective 2.10)   (a) Why does it make good sense to model the population of the nuclear bulge of M31 separately from that of its disc? (b) If asked to carry out a population synthesis of an E2 galaxy, which of the stellar categories listed below would you expect to be well represented? Explain your answer.

(i) Lower main sequence stars;

(ii) Red giants;

(iii) Upper main sequence stars;

(iv) Cepheid variables.

2.5   The formation and evolution of galaxies

2.5.1   The origin of galaxies

Where do galaxies come from? This mystery has been brought to the forefront of astronomy by advances in observational technology and a growing realization of the importance of dark matter in the Universe. Although a great deal remains uncertain, it is already quite clear that any modern investigation of galactic birth must cross the traditional boundaries of astronomy and enter the territory of **cosmology** – the study of the Universe as a whole, including its origin and evolution.

Cosmology – in particular the Big Bang, the current theoretical paradigm for describing the early evolution of the Universe – is the subject of Book 4, and it would be inappropriate, at this stage of the Course, to enter into a detailed discussion of the Big Bang. However, a familiarity with some of its features is essential to an understanding of current views on galaxy formation. Suffice it then, to note the following points that are consequences of the **Big Bang theory** and its common elaborations.

Note that the Big Bang is a theory, not an incontrovertible fact, and while it is widely agreed by cosmologists to be in good accord with observations, it is not quite universally accepted.

• The cosmic expansion that we see today, as evidenced by Hubble's law, has persisted since very early times, and the rate of expansion is decreasing due to gravitational attraction between all mass in the Universe.

• At a time shortly after the formation of the first stable atoms, long before the first stars or galaxies formed (which was probably between 1×10^{10} and 2×10^{10} years ago), the Universe was filled by a highly uniform cloud of gas that fully participated in the overall cosmic expansion. Consequently, the average density of the gas declined with time.

- At least part of this cosmic gas was made of ordinary atoms (i.e. not the non-baryonic constituent of dark matter). Of this, about 75% by mass consisted of hydrogen atoms and most of the remainder was helium, though there would have been minor traces of other light elements.

- Despite its high degree of uniformity, the cosmic gas was subject to density fluctuations. In other words, there would have been regions where the actual density departed slightly from the average.

According to one particular theory of galaxy formation, the **cold dark matter theory**, the cosmic gas referred to above consisted mainly of massive, slow-moving particles, and these make up most, perhaps all, of the dark matter inferred to be present today in the outer parts of spiral galaxies and in clusters of galaxies. The nature of this **cold dark matter** is still unclear, though other aspects of the Big Bang are used to argue that most of it cannot consist of the baryons (protons, neutrons, etc.) that are found in ordinary atomic matter. Nonetheless, ordinary atomic matter would also have been present in the gas; it perhaps accounted for somewhere between 1% and 10% of its mass.

As the expansion of the Universe progressed, the average density of the gas declined and some of the density enhancements disappeared. However, enhancements of appropriate size, including some of those shown in Figure 2.22, may have become more pronounced, thanks to their own gravitational attraction. Such **gravitational instabilities** would have created localized regions in which clouds of matter collapsed despite the general background of expansion. It is these collapsing clouds which are supposed to have been the 'seeds' of the galaxies and clusters of galaxies that surround us now. Dark matter would have played a key role here, since its effect would be to increase the instabilities (see Plate 3.37).

The steps leading from a collapsing gas cloud to a galaxy are complicated and unclear. Detailed models exist but no single model can yet claim universal acceptance, and many fundamental issues have still to be definitively resolved. Did galaxies such as the Milky Way form from the rapid collapse of a single cloud or were they the result of a more protracted process in which many smaller clouds merged together? It appears that dark matter is probably important in galaxy formation, but what exactly is its role? What would happen if there were no dark matter? Did dark matter really dominate and, if so, what were the mechanisms that allowed ordinary baryonic matter to dissipate its energy so much more effectively than dark matter that it could settle into the centres of density enhancements and thus come to dominate the visible parts of galaxies (stars and the ISM) as it seems to have done? Did such **dissipational settling** of baryonic matter occur in all collapsing density enhancements or was it biased towards the strongest? Moreover, what accounts for the very real differences that exist between the various classes of galaxies? It is pretty clear that the rates of star formation have been different in elliptical, spiral and irregular galaxies, perhaps as indicated in Figure 2.23, but what is the significance of these differences? Is it a cause or an effect? The answers to these questions, and a great many others, are still a matter of controversy. At the present time there is, perhaps, a consensus that the general picture of gravitational instability and dissipational settling in an expanding Universe dominated by dark matter is correct, and that all else is a matter of detail. However, the consensus is delicate and the future uncertain.

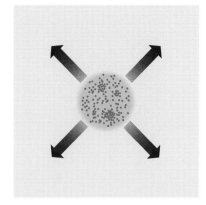
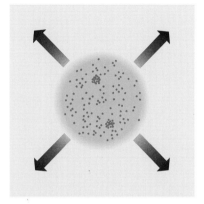
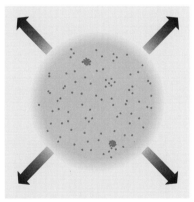

Figure 2.22 The effect of gravitational instabilities in a region of the expanding Universe dominated by dark matter. Regions of enhanced density tend to grow along with the general cosmic expansion, but if sufficiently dense they may eventually defy the expansion and collapse. In each case the number of particles in the region shown is the same and the particles themselves are a mix of baryons and dark matter particles.

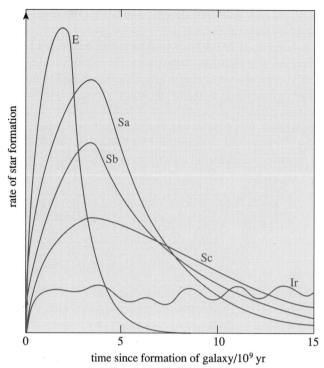

Figure 2.23 Star formation rates in different types of galaxy as a function of time. This graph is highly speculative!

One discovery that could have a significant impact on this field would be that of a **proto-galaxy** (a galaxy still condensing from the cosmic gas) or a **primeval galaxy** (a very young galaxy still illuminated by the first generation of stars). If such galaxies are to be observed, they will be at very great distances, because in order for us to receive light emitted when the Universe was very young and galaxies were forming, the light must have travelled a very great distance to be reaching us only now. Some candidates have been found – mainly distant galaxies undergoing rapid bursts of star formation, but the case for believing them to be primeval galaxies is not cast-iron. The most distant normal galaxy observed to date is at a redshift, z, of 3.428 (though quasars are seen with z values of up to $\sim$ 5). The light that we receive from it probably started its journey when the Universe was less than 15% of its present age. If proto-galaxies and primeval galaxies are only to be found further away than this, when the Universe was even younger, it may be necessary to use less direct observational techniques – these will be discussed in the next chapter.

2.5.2 *The evolution of isolated galaxies*

Returning to territory that is a little firmer, let us now consider the evolution of a galaxy that has already formed and exists as a vast collection of stars, suffused by gas, dust, magnetic fields, cosmic rays and radiation; all embedded, it seems, in an overwhelming amount of dark matter. How will such a galaxy evolve?

There are at least three important ways in which an isolated galaxy evolves. The study of each has become a specialized sub-field of extragalactic astronomy. Each is briefly described below.

Dynamical evolution

The stars in a galaxy move in orbits that are determined by the overall gravitational influence of the galaxy. Stars are tiny compared to the spaces that separate them, so collisions are rare and their effect may be neglected. However, close encounters between stars that drastically influence their orbits are more common, and can lead to a gradual redistribution of stellar orbits within a galaxy. Such a process is an example of dynamical evolution.

The investigation of the behaviour of stellar systems using Newton's laws of motion and Newton's law of gravitation constitutes the field of **stellar dynamics**. The study of the dynamical evolution of galaxies is one of the major topics within that field. Stellar dynamics is a highly technical field in which the present state of a stellar system usually depends in a detailed way on its past history. One of the most powerful ways of investigating such systems is by means of computer simulation. In a typical simulation of a galaxy, a computer is programmed with the initial positions and initial velocities of thousands of point masses, representing groups of stars, or clouds of gas and dust. It then uses Newton's law of gravitation to work out the force on each of these masses due to the attraction of all the others. Having done this it uses a formula based on Newton's laws of motion to compute the positions and velocities of the particles after a short time δt. Using these updated values of position and momentum, the whole calculation is repeated to find the configuration of the system after another step δt in time. After a great deal of computation, the various configurations can be put together to give a dynamic record of the evolution of the system. Four 'frames' from such a record are show in Figure 2.24.

What is being described here is just one particular method of simulation known as molecular dynamics. Other methods are also used.

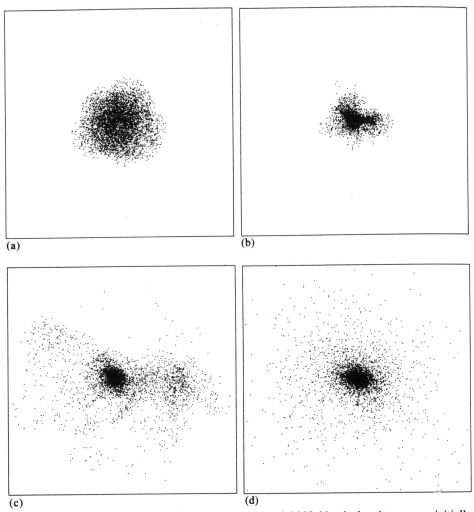

(a) (b)

(c) (d)

Figure 2.24 Four states in the collapse of a system of 5 000 identical point masses initially distributed homogeneously and moving randomly within a roughly spherical volume. Note that the system spontaneously breaks up into clumps (b), which gain so much kinetic energy in the collapse that they are flung out to great distances (c). After a series of pulsations the system settles down into a state of quasi-equilibrium (d).

On the basis of analytic investigations and computer simulations, it is expected that once an isolated galaxy has formed its first generation of stars, it will undergo rapid dynamical evolution, leading to a fairly settled state of quasi-equilibrium after just a few hundred million years (Figure 2.24d). Theoretical studies indicate that the particular quasi-equilibrium configuration adopted by any individual galaxy will depend upon the history of that galaxy. Obviously, one of the questions that most interests workers in this field concerns the conditions that lead to the observed forms of galaxies – ellipticals, lenticulars, spirals and irregulars. Are these the natural outcome of the dynamical evolution of isolated galaxies and, if so, what is it that determines the form taken by any individual galaxy? No definitive answer has yet been found, partly because the simulations are still rather crude, and partly because there are so many factors that might be relevant. However, simulation is of great value because of the insight it provides into highly complicated processes and the time they require. The time-scale to reach quasi-eqilibrium is fairly short in comparison with the estimated age of at least 10^{10} years for the oldest stars in the Milky Way (i.e. stars in globular clusters; see Chapter 1), so formation represents a relatively brief phase in the life of a galaxy. It seems likely, though, that rates of star formation (Figure 2.23) continue to change throughout the lives of spiral and irregular galaxies.

We shall have more to say about dynamical evolution and computer simulations in the next subsection when we discuss interacting galaxies. For the moment, let's leave the subject and move on to consider forms of evolution that involve the stars themselves rather than the orbits they follow.

Evolution of luminosity and spectra

It is generally suspected that when stars first started to form in galaxies they did so more-or-less simultaneously throughout the galaxy. If so, young galaxies might well have been highly luminous and probably rather blue.

ITQ 2.8 Why might you expect a galaxy filled with young stars to be blue?

This expectation is borne out by the so-called **Butcher–Oemler effect**. When very distant galaxies (where we are observing light that was emitted when the Universe was much younger than its present age) are compared with those nearby, and the effects of redshift are taken into account, the distant galaxies are found to be bluer than those nearby.

ITQ 2.9 If all the stars in the galaxy formed in a single massive burst of star formation when the galaxy was very young, how would you expect the luminosity and colour of the galaxy to evolve subsequently?

The picture painted by the last ITQ, of all the stars in a galaxy forming in a single giant burst, is almost certainly too simple to apply to any galaxy, though it might provide a crude approximation to the behaviour of elliptical galaxies, which seem to have consumed their star-forming gas (Figure 2.23). Certainly, the picture is too simple for spirals, in which star formation continues in the disc, and for irregulars, where star formation also continues, though apparently in a more fitful way. Indeed, there may in fact be no initial burst of star formation, especially if galaxies formed via the coalescence of smaller entitites of stars and gas.

In order to carry out a proper analysis of the evolution of the luminosity of a galaxy, it is necessary to model the rate at which stars of various types formed and died throughout the history of a galaxy. Then, using theoretical models of the evolution of each type, it is possible to calculate how the luminosity and the integrated spectrum of the galaxy would evolve with time. Comparing these calculations with observations allows models of stellar formation and evolution to be tested and refined.

☐ When comparing evolutionary predictions with the properties of observed galaxies, is it ever possible to observe the evolution of a single galaxy? If not, how can such comparisons be handled?

■ Galaxies evolve too slowly for changes in any one galaxy to be seen. By looking at different galaxies it may be possible, as in the case of stars, to observe individuals at different stages in their evolution.

Chemical evolution

The first stars, formed from the cosmic gas of the Big Bang, should have consisted almost entirely of hydrogen and helium. As these stars burnt themselves out, some would have exploded in supernovae, enriching their surroundings with the products of nuclear fusion. This enriched material would have contributed to the formation of later generations of stars which would, consequently, have had a higher metallicity than the earliest stars. As this process continued, both the interstellar matter in a galaxy and the stars that were embedded in it would gradually change their chemical composition. Hydrogen and helium would always be common, but the proportion of heavy elements would gradually increase.

ITQ 2.10 Apart from supernovae, what other processes would you expect to contribute to the chemical enrichment of the interstellar medium?

supernovae
stellar winds
formation of planetary nebulae
stellar flares + coronal mass ejections.

The study of chemical evolution is another highly technical field, particularly for spiral galaxies, such as the Milky Way, where rates of star formation and hence (presumably) of chemical enrichment vary from one region to another. On the basis of chemical evidence it is possible to derive models for the changing rate of star formation, at least for the solar neighbourhood. However, one major uncertainty that influences such models is the extent to which matter from outside the Milky Way may have settled into the disc over time. This raises the general issue that it may not be appropriate to regard any galaxy as entirely isolated in the way that has been done in this subsection. The closely related topic of the evolution of interacting galaxies is the final topic that we consider in this chapter.

2.5.3 The evolution of interacting galaxies

At one time, interactions between different galaxies were thought to be of little significance. Apart from a few fairly obvious cases of galaxies that were clearly undergoing some sort of collision or close encounter, it was generally assumed that galaxies evolved as isolated individuals. That view has changed drastically in the past few years, partly as a result of the impact of computer simulations.

In the 1970s, two Estonian brothers working in America, Alar and Juri Toomre, published the results of various simulations of **interacting galaxies**. They were soon followed by others and a new field of research quickly developed, aided by the availability of ever-larger computers. Some frames from one particular Toomre simulation are shown in Plate 3.14 and the corresponding astronomical object in Plate 3.13. As you can see, the relevance of the simulation to the real world seems apparent and undeniable. Other peculiar systems – including the Whirlpool Galaxy (M51), shown in Plate 3.15 – have also been modelled with great success.

The widespread recognition that interactions might be of much more general importance followed the 1983 discovery, by the Infra-Red Astronomical Satellite (IRAS), that many galaxies shine more brightly at infrared wavelengths

Computer simulation and interactions between galaxies are included in video sequence 12, which is scheduled for viewing when you reach the end of this book.

than they do at visible wavelengths. Enhanced infrared emission is frequently associated with interacting galaxies, since the interactions promote star formation which is itself accompanied by infrared emission. Yet more evidence came when it was shown that the existence of a class of quiescent elliptical galaxies called **shell galaxies** could apparently be accounted for by a process of galactic merger. A shell galaxy is shown in Figure 2.25. It appears to be an ordinary elliptical, except that it is surrounded by a number of faint shells of luminous matter. Computer simulations such as that illustrated in Figure 2.26 indicate that the merger of an elliptical with a small disc-like galaxy can lead to an oscillation of one galaxy relative to the other that 'shakes off' a series of shells very much like those that are seen.

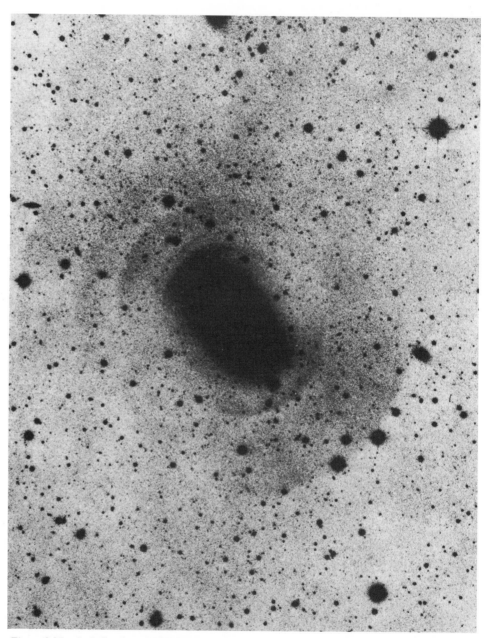

Figure 2.25   A shell galaxy, NGC 3923.

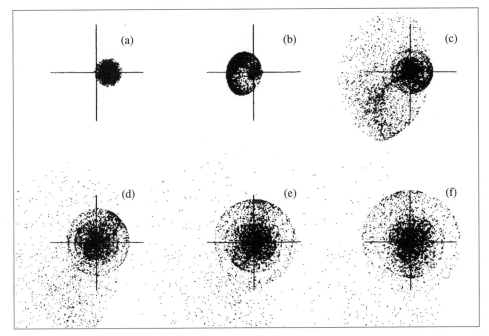

Figure 2.26 Snapshots from a computer simulation that seems to account for the existence of shell galaxies.

Identifiable shell galaxies are a very special class of galaxy, but ordinary ellipticals are very common. Could ordinary ellipticals themselves be a result of mergers? It has been known for many years that ellipticals occur more frequently in regions where galaxies are more densely clustered together. Partly for this reason and partly because the orbits of stars in ellipticals are randomly oriented compared with the well-ordered orbits in the discs of spirals, it has been suggested that many ellipticals may have formed from the merger of other galaxies, possibly from disc-like galaxies such as spirals and lenticulars. Simulations also show that mergers can produce slowly-rotating luminous ellipticals from two fainter, more rapidly rotating, ones. The notion of collisions playing a major role in producing the galaxies we see today becomes all the more plausible when it is remembered that cosmic expansion (discussed in Book 4) means that galaxies would have been more tightly packed together in the past than now, so the likelihood of interaction, collision and merger might well have been much greater then.

It is tempting to think that *all* primeval galaxies might have been discs and *all* ellipticals the result of mergers. Although this seems unlikely to have been the case, there can be no doubt that studies of interactions and mergers, together with their influence on galactic evolution, will continue to be an important part of modern astronomy for some time.

Summary of Section 2.5 and SAQs

1   Galaxies are thought to have formed as a result of density fluctuations in the expanding cosmic gas produced by the Big Bang.

2   Gravitational instabilities may have triggered the collapse of clouds of dark matter which contained traces of ordinary baryonic matter. Dissipational settling would have allowed the baryonic matter to accumulate at the centres of such clouds where it might be detected in the form of a collapsing proto-galaxy.

3   The development of young primeval galaxies into the mature galaxies we see today, can be studied in a number of ways. Dynamical studies, often based on computer simulations, are being pursued, together with chemical and spectral studies which relate to the rates of star formation and other features of stellar evolution theory.

4   There is considerable evidence that the interaction of galaxies (including mergers and collisions) can be of great importance. It almost certainly accounts for many of the distorted peculiar galaxies that are observed and it may be of more general importance in explaining the prevalence of ellipticals in many clusters of galaxies.

SAQ 2.11 (Objective 2.11)   Figure 2.27 shows a sort of Hertzsprung–Russell (H–R) diagram which has been divided into cells corresponding to various ranges of temperature and luminosity. Within some of the cells a block has been drawn. The size of each block is proportional to the number of stars in a certain galaxy that fall within the given range of temperature and luminosity. The three parts of Figure 2.27 represent, in a random order, population models for various stages in the evolution of a galaxy that formed all its stars in one huge burst of star formation. Write down the correct chronological sequence of the diagrams and explain the effects that such evolution would have on the appearance of the galaxy.

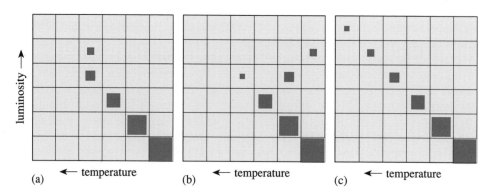

Figure 2.27 Galactic populations on a cellular H–R diagram. Note that these are not in chronological sequence.

SAQ 2.12 (Objective 2.11)   It is assumed that the primordial cosmic gas from the Big Bang was almost devoid of heavy elements (i.e. its metallicity was almost zero). However, observations of even the oldest stars never reveal any stars with such very low metallicity. How would you explain this state of affairs?

Objectives for Chapter 2

After studying Chapter 2 (and any associated audio, video or TV material) you should be able to:

2.1   Give brief definitions of the terms, concepts and principles listed below.

2.2   Sketch the main Hubble classes of galaxies and describe the distinguishing features of each class.

2.3   Compare and contrast the properties of the various Hubble classes.

2.4   Explain some implications and limitations of the basic Hubble classification and describe some of its common extensions.

2.5 List a number of methods of measuring astronomical distances, state which of them specifically relate to objects beyond the Milky Way, and describe and use some of those methods in detail.

2.6 Write down Hubble's law. Comment on the problems associated with the determination of Hubble's constant and quote the current range of values for that constant.

2.7 Use the definition of redshift and the given form of Hubble's law to determine the distances of objects beyond the Milky Way.

2.8 Understand the significance of surface brightness and isophotes in assessing galactic luminosities and sizes.

2.9 Describe a variety of techniques for determining the masses of galaxies, and comment on the results provided by those techniques (including their relevance to dark matter).

2.10 Understand, in qualitative terms, the method of stellar population synthesis in galaxies and comment on its value.

2.11 Describe some recent studies of galactic evolution (spectral, chemical and dynamical) and comment on their significance.

List of scientific terms, concepts and principles used in Chapter 2

Term	Page	Term	Page	Term	Page
active galaxy	49	gravitational instability	79	primeval galaxy	80
apparent surface brightness	71	Hubble classes	51	prolate spheroid	55
barred galaxy	51	Hubble classification scheme	51	proto-galaxy	80
Big Bang theory	78	Hubble types	51	redshift	68
binary galaxy	74	Hubble's constant	69	rotation curve	73
brightest cluster galaxy	67	Hubble's law	69	semi-major axis	51
Butcher–Oemler effect	82	integrated spectrum	76	semi-minor axis	51
calibration problem	62	interacting galaxies	83	shell galaxy	84
cD galaxy	57	irregular galaxy	51	Small Magellanic Cloud	63
Cepheid variable method	63	isophote	71	spiral galaxy	51
cluster (of galaxies)	67	Large Magellanic Cloud	60	standard candle	60
cold dark matter	79	lenticular galaxy	51	standard candle method	61
cold dark matter theory	79	light curve	62	stellar dynamics	81
cosmology	78	Local Group	64	triaxial ellipsoid	55
dark matter	72	mass to light ratio	76	Tully–Fisher relation	67
dissipational settling	79	morphology (of a galaxy)	50	Type Ia supernova	65
dwarf elliptical galaxy	54	normal galaxy	49	unbarred galaxy	51
dynamical evolution (of a galaxy)	56	oblate spheroid	55	velocity dispersion	74
ellipsoid	55	peculiar galaxy	57	Virgo cluster	64
elliptical galaxy	51	period–luminosity relationship	63	virial theorem	74
flattening factor	51	planetary nebula luminosity function	66		
galactic distance ladder	61	population synthesis	76		

Chapter 3
Starburst and active galaxies

Prepared for the Course Team by Dave Adams

Contents

3.1 Introduction

Even on images taken with the most modern equipment on a large telescope, you would find it difficult to pick out the galaxies now known as 'starburst' and 'active' from the other more normal galaxies. But if your telescope were equipped to examine the *spectra* of the galaxies, then the starburst and active galaxies would stand out. Normal galaxies are made up of stars that have similarities to the stars in our galaxy, and spiral galaxies additionally have a close similarity to our own galaxy in their gas and dust content. Starburst and active galaxies show extra emission of radiation, and this is most apparent from the spectra.

Starburst galaxies are spirals that show spectral peculiarities and an excess of radiation compared with normal spirals. This extra radiation comes from extended regions in the disc, and is believed to be the result of bright stars that have formed recently (within the last few million years) and their associated HII regions. The name refers to a recent burst of star formation; the name itself is relatively new, and will not be found in many textbooks, but starburst galaxies have been studied along with normal galaxies for some considerable time.

Starburst galaxies are quite abundant, and include some fairly nearby galaxies: two are found within 2 Mpc of the Milky Way.

Active galaxies are more remarkable and include, as you will see, Seyfert galaxies, quasars, BL Lacertae (BL Lac) objects and radio galaxies. They were discovered separately and at first seemed quite different, but they all have some form of spectral peculiarity. There is also evidence in each case that a very large amount of energy is released in a region that is *tiny* compared with the size of the galaxy, and so they are classified together. It is usually found that the tiny source region can be traced to the nucleus of the galaxy, so the origin of the excess radiation is attributed to the **active galactic nucleus** or **AGN**. An active galaxy may be regarded as a normal galaxy *plus* an AGN with its attendent effects.

Active galaxies seem to be quite rare. Only two have been found among the several hundred galaxies in the region of space extending out to the distance of the Virgo cluster.

Whether every galaxy goes through an active phase in its lifetime, or whether active galaxies have always been marked as 'special' is not clear. We have been aware of these objects for only 20 or 30 years, and the galaxies have been around for at least 10^{10} years. So the fact that we observe a small percentage of galaxies in an active phase can be explained by supposing that, for the same small percentage of each galaxy's lifetime, it is active. But it can also be explained by supposing that a small subset of galaxies are active for a longer time. (A further complication is that some nearby galaxies, including our own, show evidence of activity on a less powerful scale, but we shall concentrate on the prominent and powerful active galaxies.)

The **engine** that powers the AGN, the tiny nucleus of the active galaxy, is the greatest mystery of all. It has to produce power at 10^{11} or more times that of our own Sun, but it has to do this in a region little larger than the Solar System. To explain this remarkable phenomenon, a remarkable explanation is required. This has proved to be within the imaginative powers of astronomers, who have proposed that the engine consists of an *accreting massive black hole*, around which gravitational energy is converted into radiation.

This chapter deals with the following aspects of starburst and active galaxies. Section 3.2 covers the spectra of galaxies in detail, and shows how starburst and active galaxies stand out spectrally. It then describes overall spectra quantitatively. Section 3.3 describes a wider range of observed properties of starburst galaxies, and of the various types of active galaxy. It mentions the evidence for an AGN where appropriate. Section 3.4 explains why an AGN is both small and highly luminous, and shows you how to calculate both size and luminosity, and shows how the spectral properties of the AGN follow from these features. Section 3.5 discusses the accreting massive black hole model, which may explain the workings of the engine that powers the AGN. Section 3.6 describes quasars in more detail, and shows how they can be used to probe the farthest reaches of the Universe. The chapter is structured by class of galaxy, not by individual object.

TV programme 7 *Jets and black holes*, and audio band 3 *Spectra of active galaxies*, are both related to this chapter. You should listen to the audio band at the end of Section 3.2. You can watch TV programme 7 at any stage in your study of this chapter, though the later the better.

3.2 The spectra of galaxies

This Section reviews what you have already encountered about the spectra of stars and galaxies. The topic will be further developed to equip you to appreciate the spectra of starburst and active galaxies.

A star's spectrum normally consists of a continuous thermal distribution with absorption lines cut into it (Figures 3.1). As you may recall from Book 1, it is possible to learn a lot about the star from a study of these absorption lines. The spectrum of an **HII region** will not be familiar to you. In the optical region it consists of just a few emission lines (Figure 3.2). You learned about HII regions as part of the interstellar medium in Book 1, Chapter 5. They make a major contribution to the spectra of galaxies because they are very bright.

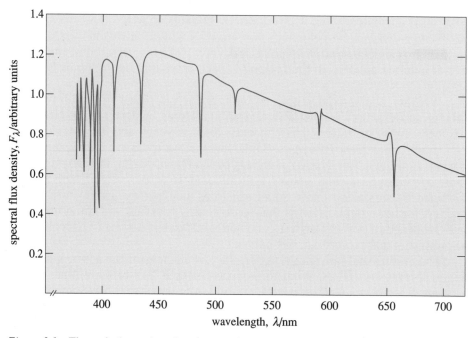

Figure 3.1 The optical wavelength spectrum of a star shown as a spectral trace. Most modern instruments produce a spectral trace directly.

ITQ 3.1 List what can be learned about a star from its spectral lines.

The spectra of stars and HII regions extend far beyond the optical region. Figure 1.24 in Book 1 shows the spectrum of the Sun extending to ultraviolet, X-ray, infrared and radio wavelengths. The majority of the Sun's radiation is concentrated into the optical part of its spectrum, but this is not the case for starburst and active galaxies, for which it is necessary to consider all the observed wavelength ranges. We shall call this the **broadband spectrum** (or **overall spectrum**), to distinguish it from the optical spectrum. You will recall that the word *optical* means visible wavelengths plus the near ultraviolet and near infrared wavelengths. Really, the optical spectrum is a detail of the overall spectrum, albeit an important detail.

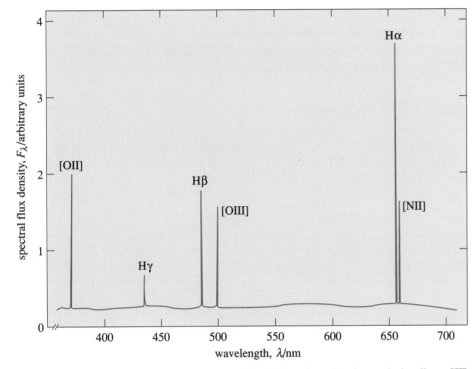

Figure 3.2 The schematic spectrum of a typical HII region, showing emission lines. HII denotes a singly ionized hydrogen atom, NII represents a singly ionized nitrogen atom, and OII and OIII denote singly and doubly ionized oxygen atoms. [NII], [OIII] and [OII] denote particular spectral lines from these ions. The meaning of the brackets is explained in Subsection 3.2.1. Recall that Hα, Hβ and Hγ are some of the Balmer lines of hydrogen (Book 1, Subsection 2.3.2).

The spectrum of a normal galaxy is the composite spectrum of the stars and gas that make up the galaxy. Some of the absorption lines of the stars and some of the emission lines of the gas can be discerned in the galaxy's spectrum. As well as being able to work out the mix of stars that make up the galaxy, we can measure the Doppler shifts of these spectral lines and so work out the motions of the galaxy (see Subsections 1.2.5 and 2.4.2).

In the case of starburst and active galaxies, the spectrum shows features *additional* to those of normal galaxies, and it is from these features that the galaxy can be picked out.

3.2.1 Normal, active and starburst galaxies: line spectra

Normal galaxies

Normal galaxies are made up from stars and (in the case of spiral and irregular galaxies) gas and dust. Their spectra consist of the sum of the emission of these components.

The optical spectra of normal stars are continuous spectra overlaid by absorption lines (Figure 3.1). There are two factors to consider when adding up the spectra of a number of stars to produce a galaxy spectrum.

First, different stars have different absorption lines in their spectra. When the spectra are added together, the absorption lines are diluted because a line in one spectrum may not appear in the other spectra.

Second, Doppler shifts can affect all spectral lines. All lines from a galaxy share the redshift of the galaxy. In addition, effects from the internal motions of the galaxy produce Doppler shifts. The absorption lines become broader and shallower. Figure 3.3 explains how this **Doppler broadening** comes about. Motion towards the observer produces a blueshift, and motion away from the observer produces a redshift. In general, if the galaxy is rotating or moving chaotically with a range of speeds of Δv, then the lines will be broadened by an amount $\Delta \lambda$:

$$\Delta \lambda / \lambda \simeq \Delta v / c \qquad\qquad (3.1)$$

where c is the speed of light, and λ is the mean wavelength. It is normal to express **line broadening** in terms of Δv, expressed in units of $km\,s^{-1}$. So a galaxy rotating about its centre will produce a spectrum in which the lines are broadened by Δv. Normal galaxies have Δv values of between 100 and $300\,km\,s^{-1}$.

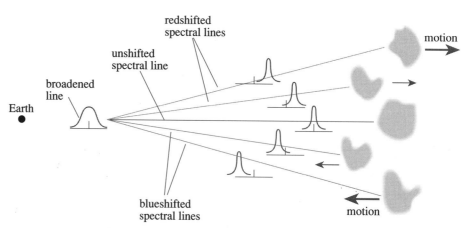

Figure 3.3 Schematic diagram to show Doppler broadening. The case of an emission line is shown; absorption lines can be similarly broadened.

HII regions in spiral and irregular galaxies shine brightly and contribute to the spectrum of the galaxy. The optical spectrum of an HII region consists mainly of emission lines, as in Figure 3.2. When such spectra are added together there are no line dilution effects, because there are only a few lines from HII regions. There are Doppler shift effects, however, as described for normal galaxies, and hence the emission lines are broadened by about the same amount as the stellar absorption lines (cf Figure 3.3).

ITQ 3.2 From Figure 1.11, estimate the broadening of lines from our own galaxy in $km\,s^{-1}$ if it were observed edge-on by an astronomer situated in a distant cluster of galaxies.

One more feature of emission lines from HII regions needs mention, and that is the presence of so-called **forbidden lines**, as opposed to the rest, which are called *allowed* lines. Most spectral lines that are seen astronomically can be produced in regions of either high or low gas density. Forbidden lines are produced only in regions of very low density; this is because, at higher densities, the excited states responsible for their production are so long-lived that normally the atom or ion will be *collisionally* de-excited by another before emission can occur. Forbidden lines are not observed in the laboratory. When they are observed astronomically, we can be sure that they have been produced in a region of extremely low density. They are prominent in the spectra of both starburst and active galaxies and are denoted by square brackets [ ]. Strong forbidden lines seen in HII regions include [NII] and [OIII] (Figure 3.2).

The optical spectrum of an elliptical galaxy is a continuous spectrum with absorption lines. Only a few absorption lines occur in a sufficient range of star types to be apparent in the spectrum, and these lines are broadened and made shallow by Doppler shifts. The overall spectrum looks like that of a K type (fairly cool) star because cool stars dominate the population.

The optical spectrum of a spiral galaxy consists of the continuous spectrum from starlight with a few shallow absorption lines from stars, plus a few rather weak emission lines from the HII regions (Figure 3.4). Note that the Hα line in normal spiral galaxies is a result of absorption from stars and emission from HII regions.

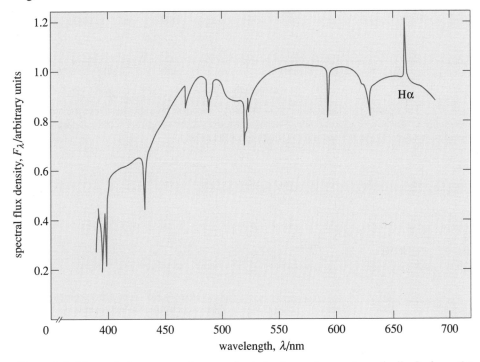

Figure 3.4 The optical spectrum of a normal spiral galaxy, shown schematically. It shows the normal absorption lines plus a weak emission line. Emission lines are more common in the spectra of spiral galaxies than in the spectra of elliptical galaxies. (Because of the overall motion of the galaxies, a particular spectral line is not necessarily at the same wavelength in all the Figures in which it appears.)

ITQ 3.3 Why has there been no mention of dust so far?   *Does not emit at optical wavelengths - significantly at far infra-red.*

What about the other types of region in the interstellar medium? No other components of the interstellar medium, apart from supernova remnants, emit in the optical, and they are faint compared with stars and HII regions.

Active and starburst galaxies

Figures 3.5 and 3.6 show schematic optical spectra for a starburst galaxy and an active galaxy, respectively. It is immediately apparent that the emission lines are stronger in both of these spectra than in the spectrum of a normal galaxy of Figure 3.4. It is as if a region producing strong emission lines had been added to the spectrum of Figure 3.4.

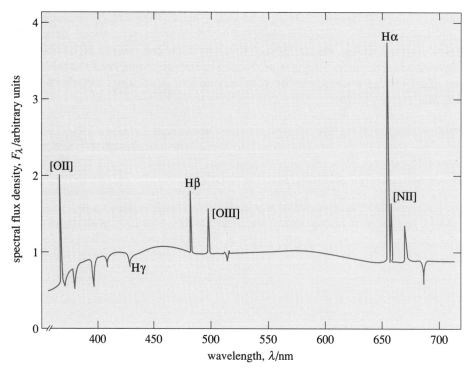

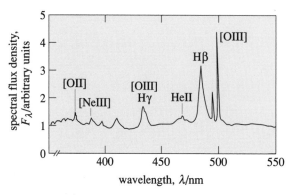

Figure 3.5 The optical spectrum of a starburst galaxy shown schematically. Note the strong emission lines, which have approximately the same width as those in normal spiral galaxies. The line-width is caused by the normal internal motions of the galaxy.

Figure 3.6 The schematic optical spectrum of an active galaxy. Note the strong and broad emission lines.

On careful examination of Figures 3.5 and 3.6, a difference in line-widths can be discerned. In Figure 3.5, the emission lines have widths little greater than those in normal spiral galaxies. The emission lines from an active galaxy are noticeably broader (Figure 3.6). So in Figure 3.5, it is as if extra HII regions have been superimposed on the spectrum of a normal spiral galaxy. The spectrum in Figure 3.6 can be regarded as the addition of a normal galaxy spectrum and emission from a gaseous region that is peculiar in that it produces *wide* emission lines.

To explain the width of the emission lines of Figure 3.6, it is necessary to consider the Doppler shift effects. Suppose that the gas producing the emission lines is in internal motion. Those regions of gas approaching the observer will appear with blueshifted lines, and those moving away from the observer will have redshifted lines, as indicated in Figure 3.3. Whether the internal motion is a rotation, an infall, an outflow, or just turbulence makes no difference; the net effect will be a broadened line whose width is proportional to the range of velocities present. When the velocities needed to explain the widths of the active galaxy lines are calculated, a range of several thousand kilometres per second is found. These are very large velocities indeed, and imply that large amounts of kinetic energy are tied up in the gas motions.

3.2.2 Normal, active and starburst galaxies: broadband spectra

The broadband spectrum is the spectrum over all the observed wavelength ranges. To plot the overall spectrum of any object it is necessary to choose logarithmic axes.

☐ Why use logarithmic axes?

■ Because both the spectral flux density, F_λ, and the wavelength vary by many powers of 10.

In Book 1, Chapter 1, you learned that F_λ is measured in watts per square metre of telescope area, per micrometre of wavelength bandwidth ($W\,m^{-2}\,\mu m^{-1}$). Figure 3.7 shows the overall spectrum of the Sun: it has a strong peak at optical wavelengths, with very small contributions at X-ray and radio wavelengths.

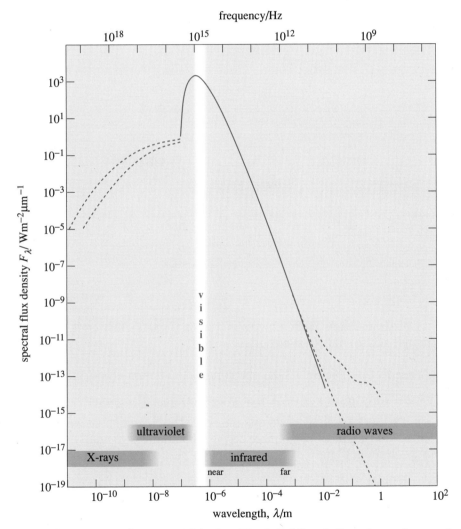

Figure 3.7 The overall spectrum of the Sun. The dashed lines indicate the maximum and minimum in regions where the flux density varies. This is a version of Figure 1.24 in Book 1, Chapter 1. Note that the microwave region is taken to be part of the radio wave region.

Normal galaxies

Figure 3.8 shows schematically the overall spectrum of a normal spiral galaxy. It resembles that of the Sun, although the peak occurs at a slightly longer wavelength than for the Sun, and there are relatively greater fluxes at X-ray, infrared and radio wavelengths.

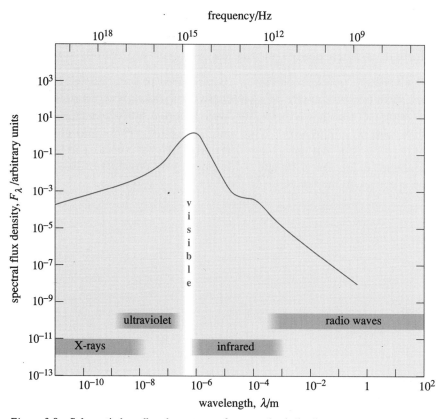

Figure 3.8 Schematic broadband spectrum of a normal spiral galaxy.

ITQ 3.4 List (from Book 1) the objects in a normal galaxy that emit at (a) X-ray, (b) infrared and (c) radio wavelengths.

However, it seems from Figure 3.8 that the dominant radiation is optical.

Broadband spectra: the dominant wavelength

In relation to Figure 3.8 we have said that the optical is the dominant wavelength region. Can we find a way of being more certain about this, particularly when the broadband spectrum in Figure 3.8 is less obviously peaked than the one in Figure 3.7?

Let's consider the power received per unit area of telescope, over a waveband of width $\delta\lambda$. The flux density F is then

$$F = F_\lambda \delta\lambda \tag{3.2}$$

(remember that F_λ is power (watts) per unit area per unit wavelength interval). Suppose we wish to compare the value of F at X-ray wavelengths with the value of F at radio wavelengths, keeping $\delta\lambda$ fixed. In this case, $\delta\lambda$ would be a *far* smaller fraction of the radio wavelength range than of the X-ray wavelength range, and therefore a plot of F versus λ would under-represent the radio range.

We can compensate for this by multiplying $\delta\lambda$ by λ, to 'boost' the longer wavelength ranges. Thus, in place of Equation 3.2 we have

$$\lambda F = F_\lambda(\lambda\delta\lambda) = \lambda F_\lambda \times \delta\lambda \qquad (3.3)$$

The product **lambda eff lambda**, λF_λ, is thus a useful quantity when we are comparing widely separated parts of a broad, smooth spectrum.

So if the spectrum in its normal form of F_λ versus λ is replotted in the form of λF_λ versus λ, then the highest points of λF_λ will indicate the wavelength regions of maximum power received from the source. So broadband spectra are more informative when plotted in this way. (If you are reading around the subject, you may encounter fF_f spectra, where f is frequency; quite simply, $fF_f = \lambda F_\lambda$.)

In Figure 3.9, λF_λ has been plotted versus λ for the normal galaxy overall spectrum of Figure 3.8, and it can be clearly seen that this curve has a peak at optical wavelengths, confirming what was suspected. The same conclusion would apply to the Sun, but not to starburst and active galaxies as you will see if you look ahead to Figures 3.10 and 3.11. From now onwards in this chapter, broadband spectra will be plotted as λF_λ versus λ.

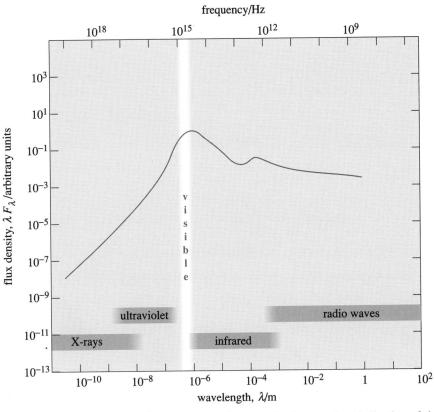

Figure 3.9 The schematic λF_λ spectrum of a normal galaxy, and an indication of the wavelength regions referred to in the text.

You may have found this discussion of λF_λ difficult. If so, don't worry about the justification, but just accept that a λF_λ plot allows you to compare widely differing wavelengths fairly, whereas an overall spectrum plotted in F_λ units does not.

ITQ 3.5 Calculate λF_λ fluxes in W m^{-2} in the radio, the far infrared and the X-ray regions, given the F_λ and λ values listed in the table on the right. Which wavelength region dominates?

Region	λ	F_λ/W m^{-2} μm^{-1}
radio	10 cm $10^5 \mu m$	10^{-28}
far IR	100 μm	10^{-23}
X-ray	10^{-10} m $10^{-4}\mu m$	10^{-20}

Far infrared dominates

Radio 10^{-23} W m^{-2}
Far IR 10^{-21} W m^{-2}
X-Ray 10^{-24} W m^{-2}

ITQ 3.6 Two galaxies at the same distance are observed. Both have broad, smooth spectra. Galaxy A is seen at optical wavelengths (around 500 nm), and yields a spectral flux density $F_\lambda = 10^{-29}$ W m^{-2} μm^{-1}; it is not detected at around 100 μm. Galaxy B appears fainter in the optical and gives $F_\lambda = 10^{-30}$ W m^{-2} μm^{-1} around 500 nm, and the same value at around 100 μm in the far infrared. Which (on these data) is the more luminous galaxy?

Galaxy B more luminous

Starburst and active galaxies

Figures 3.10 and 3.11 show overall λF_λ spectra of a starburst and an active galaxy, respectively. Immediately you can see that the energy distributions of these galaxies are different from that of a normal galaxy (Figure 3.9).

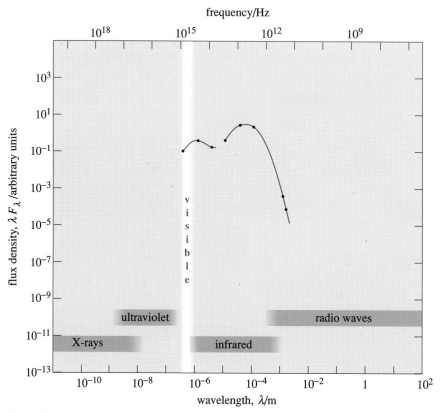

Figure 3.10 The broadband spectrum of the starburst galaxy M82, plotted as λF_λ.

By looking for the maxima in these curves, it can be seen that in the case of the starburst galaxy the dominant emission is in the far infrared, whereas in the case of this particular active galaxy (3C 273) it is in the X-ray and ultraviolet regions. In other active galaxies the infrared emission is dominant. The galaxies emit a normal amount of starlight in the optical, so they must emit several times this amount of energy at infrared and other wavelengths – this is another feature that distinguishes starburst and active galaxies from normal galaxies. It means that we have to account for *several times* the total energy output of a normal galaxy, and possibly a great deal more. A normal galaxy contains 10^{10} to 10^{11} stars, so we need an even larger energy source for active and starburst galaxies.

The term **spectral excess** is used to refer loosely to the prominence of infrared and other wavelength regions in the broadband spectra of starburst and active galaxies.

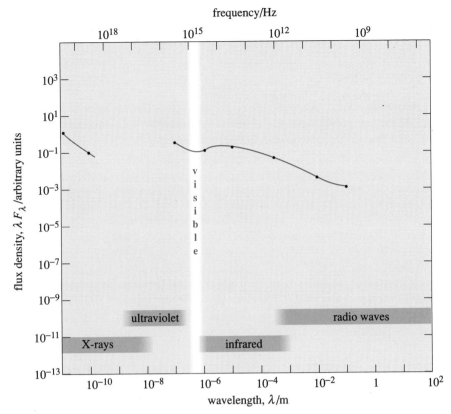

Figure 3.11 The broadband spectrum of an active galaxy, the quasar 3C 273, plotted as λF_λ.

It will now be useful to listen to audio band 3, Spectra of active galaxies, *which goes over the contents of Section 3.2.*

Summary of Section 3.2 and SAQs

1   A normal elliptical galaxy is made mainly of stars, and has an optical spectrum that looks rather like a stellar spectrum, with rather faint absorption lines. There is very little radiation at X-ray, infrared and radio wavelengths.

2   A normal spiral galaxy has an optical spectrum that is the composite of its stars (which show absorption lines) and its HII regions (which show rather weak emission lines). Again the absorption lines appear washed out, and there is little radiation at X-ray, infrared and radio wavelengths.

3   A starburst galaxy has an optical spectrum that is similar to that of a normal spiral galaxy, with additional strong but not broadened emission lines, presumably from extra HII regions.

4   An active galaxy has an optical spectrum that is the composite of the spectrum of a normal galaxy and powerful additional radiation. The additional radiation is characterized by broad emission lines in the optical.

5   To judge a broadband spectrum fairly, it is necessary to use a λF_λ plot.

6   The broadband spectra of normal galaxies peak in the optical.

7   The broadband spectra of starburst galaxies reach a maximum in the far infrared.

8   The broadband spectra of active galaxies reach a maximum at wavelengths other than the optical.

SAQ 3.1 (Objective 3.2)   Suppose that a galaxy has emission lines in its optical spectrum. A line of wavelength 654.3 nm is broadened by 2.0 nm. Estimate the motions of the gas giving rise to the broadened spectral line. Is it likely to be a normal galaxy?

SAQ 3.2 (Objective 3.3)   Suppose that an unusual galaxy has broadband spectral flux densities F_λ at wavelengths 500 nm, 5 μm and 50 μm, of 10^{-27}, 10^{-28}, and 10^{-28} W m^{-2} μm^{-1}, respectively. By calculating λF_λ, comment on whether it is likely to be a normal, a starburst, or an active galaxy.

SAQ 3.3 (Objectives 3.2 and 3.3)   A particular galaxy gives a large flux of X-rays. One astronomer believes it to be a galaxy that happens to contain a large number of separate X-ray stars. Another astronomer believes that the X-rays indicate an active galaxy. How, by measuring the spectrum of the galaxy, could you prove one person correct and the other wrong?

3.3   Other observations of starburst and active galaxies

Much could be written about these observations, which have occupied the attention of many astronomers over the past 20 to 40 years. To avoid a lengthy and 'botanical' treatment, you will be told only about the observations and ideas currently believed to be important. The whole topic of active and (particularly) starburst galaxies is still being researched, and it could turn out that features currently thought to be unimportant may be crucial to a more complete understanding.

3.3.1   Starburst galaxies

Starburst galaxies were not discovered suddenly, but have been recognized as interesting for many years. The name 'starburst' is relatively recent; in the past they have been called 'hot spot' and 'Irr II' galaxies.

The best known starburst galaxy is M82. This galaxy is nearby, lying just outside the Local Group in a group of galaxies that includes the bright spiral M81. The overall spectrum of M82 was shown in Figure 3.10, and a quick inspection of this will convince you that this galaxy shows a dominant emission in the far infrared part of the spectrum. Figure 3.12 shows the strong, narrow emission lines in the optical. Therefore the galaxy satisfies the spectral criteria for starburst galaxies discussed in Section 3.2.

A photograph of M82 at visible wavelengths is shown in Plate 3.17; note its cloudy appearance. Figure 3.13 shows contour maps of the brightness of the galaxy in the infrared. These are of interest because infrared radiation is able to penetrate the dust that is certainly present in this galaxy, and because the longer wavelength infrared is probably from heated dust. It is apparent from Figure 3.13 that whatever is emitting brightly in the infrared is an extended region concentrated towards the centre of the galaxy. The region has an extent of about 1 arcmin. It is this considerable extent of the strongly emitting region that characterizes a starburst galaxy, and it is found that the region of strong emission *lines* is similarly extended. As you will find below, active galaxies are quite different, so that this size is a distinguishing feature of starburst galaxies.

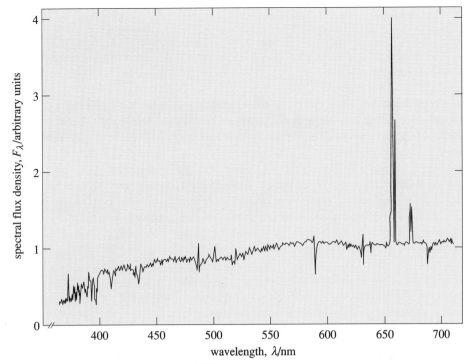

Figure 3.12 The optical spectrum of M82.

Other nearby starburst galaxies are NGC 253 (Plate 3.18) and NGC 3077. Both show strong emission lines and an extended region of infrared emission. Many distant galaxies with a dominant infrared luminosity have been discovered by the infrared-sensing satellite IRAS (Plate 1.33b), and these are suspected of being even brighter examples of the starburst phenomenon.

3.3.2 *What makes a starburst galaxy unlike a normal spiral?*

Our understanding of a starburst galaxy is that something has caused a recent (within the last few million years) burst of star formation in the central region. Star formation is expected if some of the interstellar gas is compressed. This is likely to occur if the galaxy is disturbed by another massive body. In the case of M82, it is probable that a tidal encounter with the galaxy M81 occurred a few million years ago, and it is possible this was responsible for triggering the burst of star formation.

The effect of a burst of star formation is clear. Stars are formed with a range of masses. Those stars with masses greater than about $5M_\odot$ will be luminous and hot. These massive stars emit sufficient ultraviolet light to cause the existing interstellar medium to become HII regions, and the emission lines of hydrogen, oxygen and nitrogen are observed. These are the lines in Figure 3.12. Ultraviolet radiation, which penetrates the gas, will warm up surrounding dust clouds and cause them to radiate in the infrared. This radiation is revealed as the infrared peak of Figure 3.10. The extended features of Figure 3.13 come about because a starburst galaxy has many hot blue stars, distributed in space, with each one being surrounded by its own HII region. Figure 3.14 shows the above ideas in schematic form.

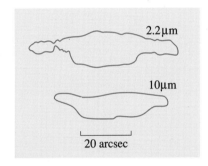

Figure 3.13 Contour maps of the infrared radiation from M82. The upper map was taken at 2.2 μm, and the lower one at 10 μm. Both maps surround the galactic centre.

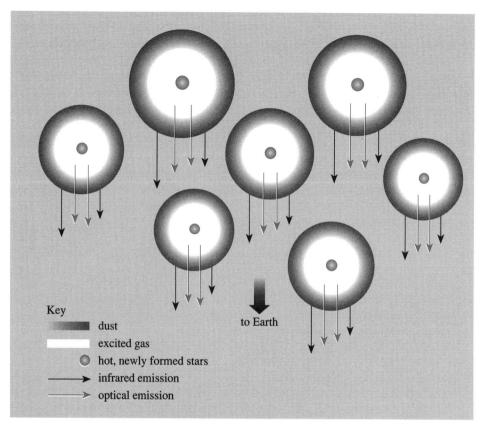

Figure 3.14 Schematic diagram of HII regions and dust in a starburst galaxy.

The hot stars are short-lived, so after a few million years the starburst is expected to fade out. The power source of a starburst is nuclear fusion in the massive stars.

3.3.3 Active galaxies

Seyfert galaxies

It was in 1943 that the American astronomer Carl Seyfert (1911–1960) drew attention to a few spiral galaxies that have unusually bright point-like nuclei in the optical. Plate 3.22 shows M77, also called NGC 1068. The bright nucleus is overexposed in the plate, but is shown schematically in Figure 3.15. The optical spectra of the nuclei of Seyfert galaxies show strong emission lines, as shown in Figure 3.16. Subsequently, it has been found that **Seyfert galaxies** show an excess of radiation in the far infrared and at other wavelengths, and even more remarkably that, at some wavelengths, this radiation is *variable*. The strong emission lines and overall spectral excess place Seyfert galaxies well into the active category. The point-like nucleus, and especially the variability, distinguish a Seyfert from the starburst galaxies. Variability is discussed in detail in Subsection 3.4.1 – suffice it to say here that the excess from a Seyfert galaxy must come from a region that is *tiny* compared with that of a starburst galaxy.

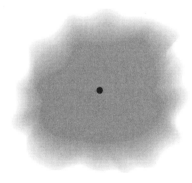

Figure 3.15 Schematic brightness map of a Seyfert galaxy at visible wavelengths. Note the strong central point source.

The emission lines from a Seyfert galaxy are wider than those from starburst galaxies. This is interpreted to indicate that the gaseous region responsible for the emission is in motion with a spread of velocities of at least $700 \, \mathrm{km \, s^{-1}}$. In the so-called type 2 Seyferts, both allowed and forbidden lines have approximately this width. In type 1 Seyferts, the forbidden lines have a width of about $700 \, \mathrm{km \, s^{-1}}$ (we shall refer to these lines as having intermediate width), but the allowed lines are broad (more than $1\,000 \, \mathrm{km \, s^{-1}}$). The widths of emission lines further distinguish Seyferts from starburst galaxies.

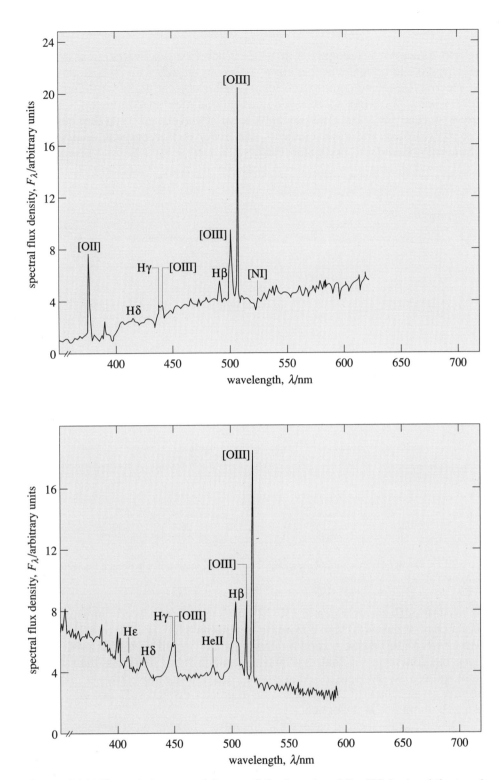

Figure 3.16 The optical spectra of the type 2 Seyfert galaxy Mkn 270 (top) and the type 1 Seyfert galaxy Mkn 290 (bottom). Note the emission lines, some of which are broader on the bottom spectrum.

The small, bright and variable nucleus in a Seyfert galaxy was the first example to be discovered of what is now termed an 'active galactic nucleus' or AGN. Much of the remainder of this chapter is concerned with AGNs.

The first **quasar** was recognized in 1963. When first discovered, quasars were seen at radio and optical wavelengths as points in the sky with unusual emission line spectra. The name comes from 'quasi-stellar objects' (QSOs), stellar in the sense of being point-like sources and quasi in that their spectra are quite unlike those of normal stars. The emission lines occur at wavelengths that turn out to be those of hydrogen and other elements that occur in astronomical sources, but significantly *redshifted* – see Figure 3.17.

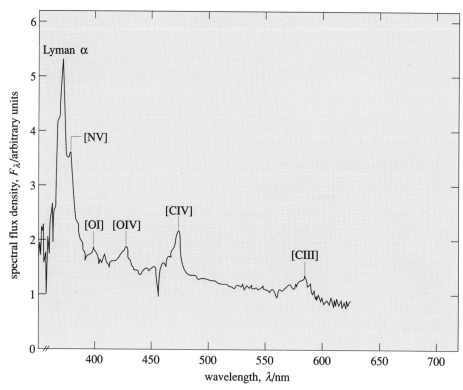

Figure 3.17   The optical spectrum of the quasar Ton 1530. Lyman α is a hydrogen line with an emitted wavelength of 121.6 nm.

The redshift of the nearest quasar (3C 273) is 0.158. This redshift corresponds to a distance of at least 400 Mpc according to Hubble's law (Equation 2.2). At this distance even the brightest known normal galaxy would be difficult to detect. Hence the conclusion is that this quasar is much more luminous than even a bright galaxy in the optical. Many other quasars are now known: all have redshifts greater than 0.158 and hence lie at greater distances. Hence all quasars are highly luminous in the optical.

Quasars show spectral excesses in the infrared and at other wavelengths, as shown in Figure 3.18. Many also show variability, and their emission lines are broad. In just a few quasars the parent galaxy has been observed as a faint extended object. The picture of a quasar that emerges is of a distant, very luminous example of the active galactic nucleus as found in a Seyfert galaxy, buried in a galaxy of normal luminosity. This is why we include quasars in the active galaxy category here. (Some books refer to 'active galaxies and quasars'.) Quasars are believed to be the most luminous examples of AGNs known. They are discussed in more detail in Section 3.6.

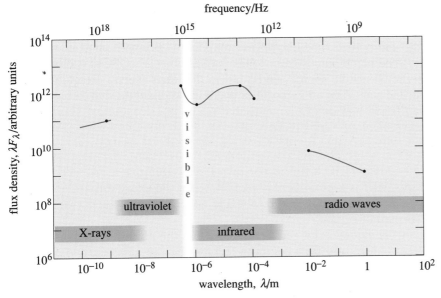

Figure 3.18   The broadband spectrum of the quasar 3C 351.

Radio galaxies

Radio galaxies were discovered in the 1950s, although it took some years to recognize the family resemblance to other active galaxies. As the name implies, radio galaxies were first observed by radio astronomy: in fact, they dominate the sky at radio wavelengths. They show enormous regions of radio emission outside the visible extent of the parent galaxy – usually these 'radio lobes' occur in pairs. The brightest radio galaxy is called Cygnus A (Plate 3.20). It is interesting that the parent galaxy of radio lobes is always an *elliptical* galaxy. It is as if the gas in spiral galaxies somehow damps any radio lobes.

Figure 3.19 shows a radio map superimposed on a visible-wavelength photograph of Cygnus A. Figure 3.20 shows a radio map of Centaurus A (see also Plate 3.19), which is the nearest but not the most powerful radio galaxy. It is an elliptical galaxy with a dust lane bisecting it, and is near enough to be photographed in detail.

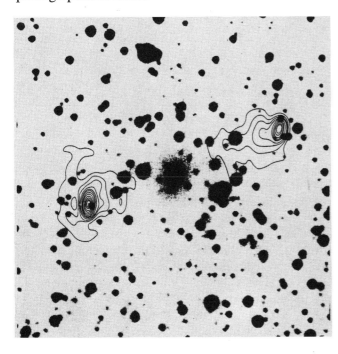

Figure 3.19   Radio contour lines of Cygnus A. The contour lines are superimposed on a visible-wavelength photograph, and the parent elliptical galaxy is the central fuzzy object.

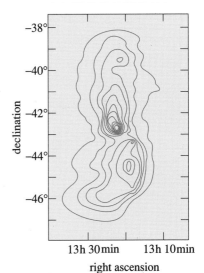

Figure 3.20 Radio contour lines of Centaurus A. Note that this radio galaxy has both inner and outer lobes. The outer radio lobes are degrees, or hundreds of kiloparsecs, across.

As well as the large and usually paired radio lobes, which are a unique feature of radio galaxies, it has been found that each radio galaxy has a point-like radio nucleus coincident with the nucleus of the parent galaxy. It is this feature that is reminiscent of other classes of active galaxies. This central object is now believed to be the seat of the activity in a radio galaxy. The nucleus shows many of the properties of other AGNs, including emission lines, excesses in other spectral regions, and variability.

M87 is such a well known radio galaxy that it must be mentioned at this point. In the optical region it appears as a giant elliptical galaxy (Plate 3.21) at the centre of the Virgo cluster. You will recall (Subsection 2.3.3) that the Virgo cluster is the closest rich cluster to our own Local Group, at a distance of only about 20 Mpc. M87 is a prominent object. Now for the exception to the general rule: M87 has only one strong radio lobe and not two! This lobe is extended as usual, but its partner is faint.

M87 shows evidence for jets extending from the point-like active nucleus out to the radio lobe. **Jets** are a common feature of radio galaxies, and are dealt with in TV programme 7. A jet is a long thin feature seen emerging from the AGN, usually at radio wavelengths. Jets often point towards the large radio lobes, and probably trace the path by which energy is being conducted from the AGN to the lobes. An example of a jet is shown in Figure 3.21. M87 is interesting in this connection, in that it has a jet that can also be seen in the visible (Plate 3.21b).

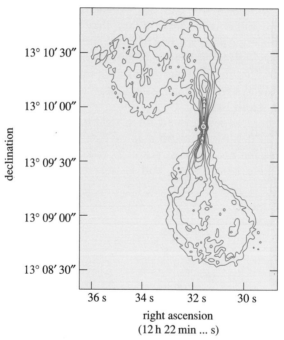

Figure 3.21   A radio map of the jet-like feature in M84.

The optical spectrum of the AGN at the centre of a radio galaxy looks very much like that of any other AGN; some radio galaxies have broad spectral lines and some have spectral lines of only intermediate width. Figure 3.22 shows an example with broad lines. But what of the luminosity of the radio lobes? When this is worked out it is found that the radio luminosity is not so large as the total luminosity of other active galaxies. This is because, for the lobes to emit radio waves at all, a radio galaxy needs a powerful AGN in order to power the magnetic field and energetic electrons that must generate the synchrotron radiation (Book 1, Subsection 5.2.5) by which the lobes shine.

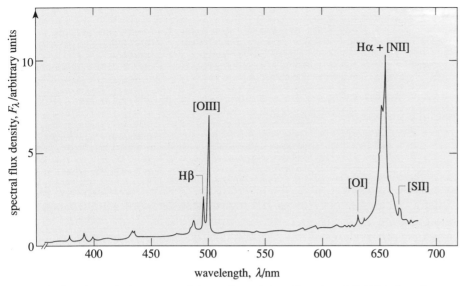

Figure 3.22 The optical spectrum of the nucleus of the radio galaxy 3C 445 (adjusted to zero redshift).

BL Lacertae objects

BL Lacertae (BL Lac) objects appear star-like, as do quasars, but show no spectral lines. At first, they were mistaken for variable stars until their spectra were studied. They are believed to lie at great distances (like quasars) on the strength of redshift observations of the emission lines of the faint galaxies in which they appear to lie. They show particularly rapid variability. BL Lacs are thought to be AGNs that are not surrounded by gas. The absence of such gas could account for the absence of spectral lines.

Summary of Section 3.3 and SAQs

1   Starburst galaxies show strong, narrow emission lines and a spectral excess at far infrared wavelengths. The region of excess emission is not point-like but occupies a significant region within the galaxy.

2   The properties of starburst galaxies in 1 are believed to result from a recent giant burst of star formation.

3   Seyfert galaxies show excesses at far infrared and other wavelengths, and strong, wide emission lines. The bright nucleus appears point-like and exhibits variability.

4   Quasars are like very distant Seyfert galaxies with very luminous nuclei. They are variable.

5   Radio galaxies are distinguished by having giant radio lobes. They have a compact nucleus like Seyfert galaxies. The compact nucleus is variable.

6   BL Lac objects are like quasars but show no emission lines. They are variable.

7   Both starburst and active galaxies show spectral excesses, but starburst galaxies possess an extended region of emission, whereas Seyferts, quasars, BL Lacs and radio galaxies show evidence for a compact nucleus.

Table 3.1 summarizes the observations of active galaxies. (Some details are added here that were not mentioned earlier.)

Table 3.1   Features of active galaxies

	Intermediate width emission lines	Broad emission lines	X-radiation	UV excess	Far infrared excess	Strong radio emission	Variability
Seyfert	yes	some cases	some cases	some cases	yes	no	yes
quasar	yes	yes	some cases	yes	yes	some cases	yes
radio galaxy	yes	some cases	some cases	some cases	yes	yes	yes
BL Lac	no	no	some cases	yes	no	some cases	yes

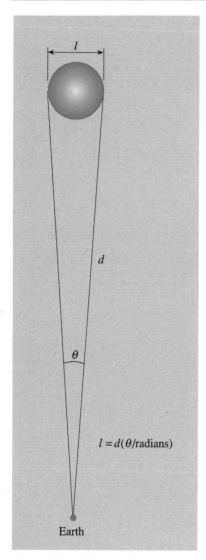

Figure 3.23 Schematic diagram to show how the linear size *l* of an AGN may be worked out from its angular size θ and distance *d*.

SAQ 3.4 (Objectives 3.2 and 3.3)   A fuzzy object is observed at low Galactic latitudes with emission lines emanating from an extended region. It is not immediately clear whether it is an HII region near the plane of our galaxy or a starburst galaxy at a distance of 10 Mpc or more. How would detailed spectroscopic observations of the emission lines help an astronomer to decide?

SAQ 3.5 (Objective 3.5)   Construct a table that compares and contrasts starburst and active galaxies in terms of the following: presence of emission lines; presence of intermediate or broad emission lines; presence of far infrared excess; presence of strong X-ray emission; variability; point-like source.

3.4   Active galactic nuclei

3.4.1   The size of AGNs: the meaning of variability

AGNs appear point-like on optical images. It is worthwhile to work out how small a region these imaging observations indicate. Optical observations from the Earth suffer from 'seeing' – this refers to the blurring of the image by atmospheric motions (TV programme 2). The result is that star-like images are always smeared by about 0.5 arcsec or more, so that it is not normally possible to tell whether a star-like image is really smaller than about 0.25 arcsec. An arcsec is 1/3 600 of a degree and there are 57.3 degrees in a radian. Hence 0.25 arcsec corresponds to an angle of $0.25/(57.3 \times 3\,600) = 1.2 \times 10^{-6}$ radian. For such a small angle, the linear diameter *l* of an object is related to its distance *d* via $l = d(\theta/\text{radians})$ (Figure 3.23). Hence for a galactic nucleus at 10 Mpc, which appears star-like, that is less than 0.25 arcsec in angular diameter θ, its linear size *l* is less than $(10 \times 10^{6}) \times (1.2 \times 10^{-6})\,\text{pc} = 12\,\text{pc}$. So, for a nearby active galaxy, we can place an upper limit of order 10 pc on its linear size. For a more distant AGN, this upper limit is correspondingly larger. So the star-like appearance of AGNs tells us that they are *much* smaller than our galaxy (whose diameter is 30 000 pc = 30 kpc).

The variability of an AGN must now be considered. The continuous spectra of most vary appreciably in brightness over a 1 year time-scale, and several vary over time-scales as short as a day, especially at X-ray wavelengths (see Figure 3.24). This variability places a much tighter constraint on the size, as you will see. Suppose that an AGN has a simple spherical shell geometry with a radius *R* (Figure 3.25). If its output is to vary appreciably, it follows that the outputs of the various pieces of the shell must change together. Suppose, again for simplicity, that a physical signal of some form is emitted from the centre of the sphere. This signal will travel at a speed not exceeding *c* and (in this simple geometry) will reach all parts of the shell at the same time, causing all parts to brighten simultaneously. But the observer on Earth (Figure 3.25) will not see an instantaneous brightening, because of the difference in light travel time from the nearest part of the sphere and from the most distant part. The observer will see a brightening that takes

$$t = 2R/c \qquad (3.4)$$

from start to finish. This argument may be inverted to state that if the observer sees a significant change in brightness in a time t, then the size of the source can be no larger than $2R = ct$. This kind of argument applies for any three-dimensional configuration.

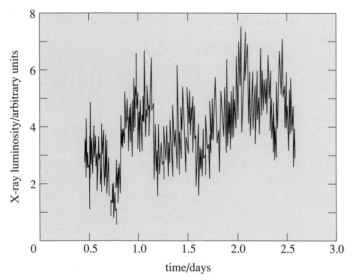

Figure 3.24 An example of X-ray variability, shown by the Seyfert galaxy MCG-6-30-15. The fastest fluctuations are spurious noise, but the 0.5 day changes are a property of the AGN.

Let's now calculate the value of $2R$ for the case of an AGN that varies on a 1 day time-scale. We have $2R = ct$, so with 1 day $= 24 \times 3\,600$ s $= 8.6 \times 10^4$ s and $c = 3.0 \times 10^8$ m s^{-1}, we obtain $2R = 2.6 \times 10^{13}$ m $= 8.4 \times 10^{-4}$ pc. This is a staggeringly small result, and is comparable with the size of the Solar System (diameter of the orbit of Pluto $= 3.8 \times 10^{-4}$ pc). The argument does not depend on the distance of the AGN. Hence the observed variability of AGNs places the strongest constraint on their size.

ITQ 3.7 An AGN at 50 Mpc appears smaller than 0.1 arcsec in an observation made by the Hubble Space Telescope, and shows variability on a 1 week time-scale. Calculate the upper limit placed on its size by (a) the angular diameter observation, and (b) the variability observation.

Other evidence also indicates the small size of AGNs. Radio astronomers operate radio telescopes with dishes placed on different continents. This so-called Very Long Baseline Interferometry (VLBI – TV programme 7) is able to resolve angular sizes one hundred or so times smaller than optical telescopes can. Even so, AGNs remain unresolved.

3.4.2 The luminosity of AGNs

It is most instructive to express the luminosity of an AGN in terms of the luminosity of a galaxy like our own. The figure may then be converted into solar luminosities, if we adopt the figure of 2×10^{10} Suns for the luminosity of our galaxy. The method presented here yields approximate numbers. It is based on

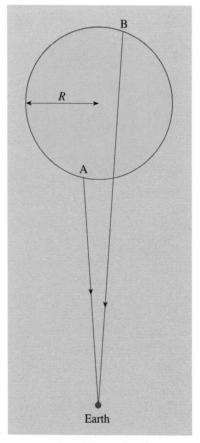

Figure 3.25 Schematic diagram to show how the time variability of an object depends on its size. Spherical shell geometry is used for simplicity.

109

the **inverse square law**, that is the dependence of flux density on $1/d^2$, where d is the distance to the object (Book 1, Equation 2.8).

Considering a Seyfert galaxy first, at optical wavelengths the point-like AGN is about as bright as the remainder of the galaxy, which radiates mainly at optical wavelengths. But the AGN also emits brightly in the ultraviolet and the infrared, and this accounts for at least three times its optical luminosity. So one concludes that for a Seyfert, the AGN has at least four times the luminosity of the rest of the galaxy.

Quasars lie at such large distances that their parent galaxies cannot normally be seen at all. For the AGN of a quasar to be visible, it must be *far* brighter than a normal galaxy. So its AGN must have a luminosity considerably greater than that of a Seyfert AGN.

In the case of a radio galaxy, the AGN may not emit as much energy in the optical as Seyfert and quasar AGNs, but an analysis of the synchrotron mechanism by which the lobes shine shows that the power input into the lobes must exceed the luminosity of a normal galaxy by a large factor, and it seems that the AGN at the centre is a likely candidate for the source of all this energy.

A similar conclusion for AGN luminosity follows for BL Lac objects.

ITQ 3.8   Calculate the luminosity of an AGN that is at a distance of 200 Mpc, and appears as bright in the optical as a galaxy like our own at a distance of 100 Mpc. Assume that one-fifth of the energy from the AGN is at optical wavelengths.

$4 \times 10^{11} L_\odot$

Hence one can conclude that AGNs in general have enormous luminosities of more than $2 \times 10^{10} L_\odot$ produced within a tiny volume. Stop to ponder this statement for a minute. The power output of the Sun is so large that it is hard to comprehend; the number 2×10^{10} is even more difficult to imagine! Putting together over 2×10^{10} Suns' worth of luminosity inside an AGN is well beyond the powers of imagination of most of us. In terms of watts, 1 Sun's worth of luminosity is about 4×10^{26} W, so a typical AGN has a luminosity of more than 8×10^{36} W. We shall adopt 10^{38} W for further discussion.

You are now in a position to appreciate the basic problem in accounting for an AGN. It produces an *enormous* amount of power (luminosity) in what is astronomically speaking a *tiny* volume. What causes such a small body to be so luminous stretches the imagination to such an extent that some people have referred to it by fanciful names such as the dragon. A more scientific name is *engine*, which we shall adopt. Current ideas about the workings of this engine are discussed in Section 3.5.

3.4.3   Infrared emission from AGNs: heated dust

So far, we have established that an AGN contains an 'engine' of very high luminosity and small size. Suppose that this engine is surrounded by a larger region of dust particles, what would we expect to see? The dust particles will be heated by the radiation from the engine until they are warm enough to radiate away an amount of energy that balances that which they receive from the engine. Any dust particles that are close to the engine will be either vaporized or blown away by radiation pressure. Dust particles farther away from the engine are exposed to a lower flux density, in accord with the inverse square law. At a sufficient distance, they will be heated to a temperature below their melting point, and at this temperature will radiate in the infrared. Hence such a dust cloud will act to convert ultraviolet or X-ray emission from the engine into infrared radiation, as in Figure 3.26. The good news is that from a very simple dust cloud model, it is easy to understand why AGNs so often emit most of their radiation in the infrared. The bad news is that this dust obscures our view of the engine, so that we cannot clearly see its own emission. Almost certainly, dust heated by the engine is observed in most AGNs, although the dust may be more irregularly distributed than in our simple model, and may have holes in it. There may also be some infrared radiation from the engine itself, and in BL Lacs it is probable that we see mainly infrared from the engine.

The dust clouds that re-radiate in the infrared are quite large, so they are believed to surround other components of the AGN, such as gas clouds. The variability that was discussed in Subsection 3.4.1 applies to radiation from the engine at X-ray and optical wavelengths (and sometimes at radio wavelengths). Variability is observed to be much slower from the warm dust, as you would expect from its greater extent.

3.4.4 Line emission from AGNs: gas clouds

Let's suppose that the engine is surrounded by gas clouds (Figure 3.27). You have already seen how common these are in our own and other galaxies, so it is reasonable to expect them to be present in at least the spiral galaxies that contain AGNs. If these gas clouds are illuminated by ultraviolet or X-rays from the AGN they will absorb the ultraviolet or X-ray energy, and will emit the characteristic lines of the gases making up the clouds. The most abundant gas in galactic clouds is hydrogen, and, sure enough, the Hα and other lines of hydrogen appear strongly in the observed spectra of AGNs.

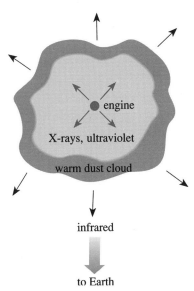

Figure 3.26 Schematic diagram to illustrate the re-radiation by a dust cloud. The same process occurs, on a smaller scale, in Figure 3.14.

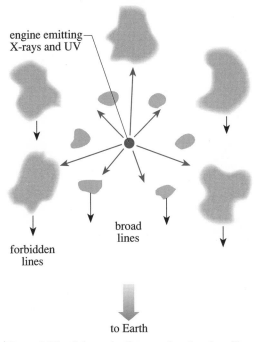

Figure 3.27 Schematic diagram showing the effect of a gas cloud surrounding an AGN; emission lines are produced. The diagram shows likely locations for the broad line region and the forbidden line region.

What about other spectral lines that might be expected? Fortunately we get clues from objects in our own galaxy, the HII regions, which consist of gas clouds illuminated by sources of ultraviolet radiation, albeit at a lower luminosity. It is found that these HII regions emit strong lines of nitrogen and oxygen in the visible, [NII] and [OIII]. Sure enough, the lines that appear in the visible spectra of AGNs turn out to be just what you would expect from a gas of normal cosmic composition surrounding an AGN.

The emission lines seen from an AGN are much broader than those seen from an HII region. It is normal to interpret these line-widths as being the result of Doppler shifts caused by the motion of the gas clouds (see Subsection 3.2.1). It is not possible to see the motion in any detail, only to estimate the spread of velocity from the observed Doppler widths. It is concluded, therefore, that the gas surrounding AGNs is in violent motion with speeds of 700 km s^{-1} or more. These violent motions are probably associated with the strong gravity surrounding an AGN. In some AGNs, the allowed lines of hydrogen are even broader than the forbidden lines [NII] and [OIII]. Forbidden lines are associated only with regions of low gas density, thus defining **forbidden line regions**, whereas allowed lines can be produced at any gas density, including within forbidden line regions. Hence it seems that the denser regions of gas are in even more violent motion than the low density regions. This makes sense if the denser regions are closer to the centre, and therefore have gained more kinetic energy from the loss of gravitational energy.

The term **broad line region** or **BLR** has been coined to refer to the region of an AGN in which the broad (greater than 1 000 km s^{-1}) allowed lines of hydrogen and other elements are produced. As you will have noted from Section 3.3, broad lines are not seen in every AGN. The general belief among astronomers is that every AGN has a broad line region, but that the broad lines are obscured by dust clouds in many cases. The forbidden line region produces lines of intermediate width (about 700 km s^{-1}). Figure 3.28 shows a possible model of an AGN.

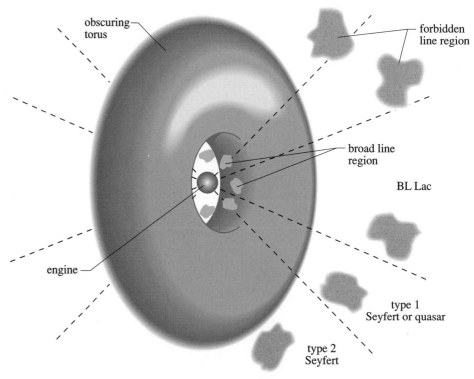

Figure 3.28   Sketch of a possible structure of an AGN. Different features will be observed from different viewing angles, as outlined at the end of this Section.

3.4.5 AGNs and radio lobes

This subsection is a description of how an AGN model can account for a radio galaxy. Suppose that, by its gravitational attraction, an AGN engine is attracting material (gas, dust or even whole stars) from its surroundings. This material will tend to form into a rotating torus around the engine. This torus will block free access to the engine except towards the sides of the page in Figure 3.28, that is, along the directions of the poles of the torus. To explain a radio galaxy, it is supposed that charged particles and magnetic fields are ejected along the poles (Figure 3.29), and interact to produce the lobes of synchrotron radio emission. Calculations of the energy input in charged particles indicate that a significant fraction of the energy output of the AGN must be given to the ejected particles and the magnetic field to account for the radio emission. Not necessarily every AGN produces this field and ejected particles, so not all active galaxies are radio galaxies.

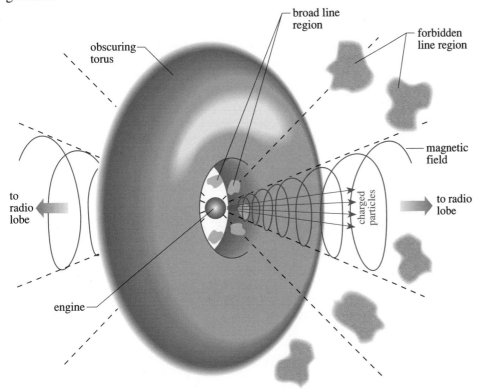

Figure 3.29 Schematic diagram to show how an AGN may eject magnetic field and relativistic electrons into distant radio lobes.

3.4.6 Naked AGNs: BL Lac objects?

Every AGN must have its engine to drive the luminosity, and the possible nature of this engine is discussed in Section 3.5. It is quite likely that, in the case of the BL Lac objects, we are seeing the engine directly, without any gas or dust clouds in the way, hence the absence of spectral lines. It is probable that the infrared radiation from a BL Lac comes from a region intimately connected with the engine, and is not re-radiation from dust. The radiation at all wavelengths from a BL Lac appears to be synchrotron radiation, so in this case the engine must produce energetic electrons and magnetic fields.

3.4.7 A Meccano set to build models of AGNs

Thus far, we have been able to explain some of the main observed characteristics of AGNs by supposing that the engine is surrounded by gas and dust – substances we see in our own galaxy. The dust yields the infrared spectral excess, and the gas yields the emission lines. It is normal to reverse these arguments and to assert that the infrared excess indicates the presence of dust, and that the emission lines indicate the presence of gas.

You are now familiar with the main components in the kit for building models of AGNs: an engine (whose workings have not yet been explained); clouds of dust; clouds of gas; and accretion processes that can organize the gas and dust into a torus-shaped structure. If the AGN contains a torus-shaped feature, then the radiation observed will depend on the direction from which the AGN is viewed.

For example, suppose that you look at the model AGN in Figure 3.28 from a direction not too far from a pole of the torus plane, then you will see X-ray and other radiation from the engine, broad lines from the broad line region, lines of intermediate width from the forbidden line region and infrared from the dust torus. You will observe the features associated with a type I Seyfert or a quasar. If you look at the same model from a direction nearer to the plane of the torus, the X-rays and the broad optical emission lines will be obscured by the torus, and you will observe the features associated with a type 2 Seyfert.

This idea of a single (unified) model observed from different angles cannot explain the presence or absence of radio lobes. Some AGNs produce the energetic electrons and magnetic fields necessary to produce synchrotron radio emission, others do not appear to. The difference is probably connected with the galaxy environment in which the AGN is situated. Elliptical galaxies contain little gas, and this seems to favour radio lobes. So the gas present in spirals must somehow damp down the energetic electrons and/or magnetic fields that produce radio emission.

Figure 3.29 shows a model of a radio galaxy AGN. Again one would expect a difference in the radiation observed from the AGN itself depending on viewing angle – indeed, some radio galaxies have broad lines in their optical spectra and others do not. Plate 3.28 shows the model as drawn by a different artist. The broad line and forbidden line regions are not shown. By comparing Figure 3.29 and Plate 3.28, you can see the differences that emerge when the model is interpreted by different astronomers.

Summary of Section 3.4 and SAQs

1   An AGN is known to be very small. Variability places the strongest constraint on size.

2   An AGN is very luminous – comparable with or greater than the luminosity of the rest of the galaxy that contains it.

3   Dust surrounding an AGN can account for its strong infrared emission.

4   Gas surrounding an AGN can account for the emission lines.

5   Gas and dust, possibly organized into a torus surrounding an engine, can be tried in various configurations to model an AGN, and these various configurations viewed from various directions can account for many of the various classes of active galaxies.

SAQ 3.6 (Objective 3.7)   Suppose that observations from the Hubble Space Telescope show the nucleus of an active galaxy to be 0.2 arcsec in diameter or smaller. If the galaxy is known to lie at 20 Mpc, estimate the upper limit that may be placed on the diameter of the AGN. How large is this in astronomical units?

SAQ 3.7 (Objective 3.7)   Suppose that the AGN in SAQ 3.6 shows a significant variation in X-rays in 1 hour. Estimate the upper limit to the size of the AGN. Why would you expect the time-scale of the infrared variations to be much longer?

SAQ 3.8 (Objective 3.4)   An active galaxy at a distance of 2 000 Mpc appears point-like, and as bright in the optical as a galaxy like our own at 50 Mpc. Estimate the luminosity of this AGN in units of $L_\odot$, if it emits one-third of its luminosity at optical wavelengths.

3.5   The nature of the beast

So far, the energetic object within an AGN has been referred to as an *engine*. This Section presents the consensus of astronomers that the engine is an accreting massive black hole.

Science deals with observations and the theories that have been thought up to explain them. A theory starts out as a hypothesis, which must then be developed into a theory by devising and carrying out a series of tests. An accreting massive black hole is the front-running hypothesis that has been put forward to explain AGNs. Despite much effort, many people would say that there is insufficient evidence to date to elevate this hypothesis to the status of a theory. Bear this in mind as you read this Section.

3.5.1   A massive black hole

A black hole is a body so massive and so small that even electromagnetic radiation, such as light, cannot escape from it. It is its *very small* size that makes it attractive as a building block for the engine that powers an AGN. You have met black holes in Book 1, Chapter 4. There they were discussed as possible endpoints to the evolution of stars with masses of a few Suns. As you will see, it turns out that much more massive black holes are needed to explain AGNs, and these are referred to as **massive black holes**. We shall avoid the question about how massive black holes came to be there in the first place.

A black hole, massive or otherwise, is such a bizarre concept that it is worth recapping. The material of which it is made is contained in a radius so small that the gravity at its 'surface' has become so strong that the escape speed exceeds the speed of light. Hence, any object that falls into it can never escape again. Even electromagnetic radiation cannot leave, hence the word 'black'. What goes on inside the black hole is academic – we cannot see. What we might see is activity close to the black hole, where gravity is strong, but not so strong as to prevent the escape of electromagnetic radiation. It is this surrounding region that Subsection 3.5.2 addresses.

The **Schwarzschild radius** has already been mentioned in Book 1, Subsection 4.4.4. This is the radius at which the escape speed is just equal to the speed of light, and is given by

$$R_S = 2GM/c^2 \tag{3.5}$$

Let us now calculate the mass M of a black hole small enough to fit inside an AGN. In Subsection 3.4.1 we showed that an AGN that varies on a 1 day time-scale must be smaller than 2.6×10^{13} m. Because many AGNs vary faster than this, especially in the X-ray region, and because in any case the AGN radius must exceed R_S, we shall adopt a size for R_S of 3.0×10^{11} m. Then, from Equation 3.5,

$$
\begin{aligned}
M &= R_S \times c^2/2G \\
&= 3 \times 10^{11} \times (3 \times 10^8)^2/(13.3 \times 10^{-11}) \, \text{kg} \\
&= 2.0 \times 10^{38} \, \text{kg}
\end{aligned}
$$

Therefore

$$M/M_\odot = 2.0 \times 10^{38} \, \text{kg}/(2.0 \times 10^{30} \, \text{kg}) = 10^8$$

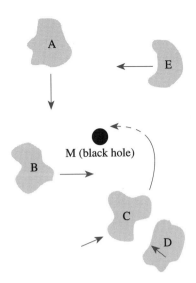

Figure 3.30 Schematic diagram of discrete gas clouds falling towards a black hole. Clouds C and D are shown colliding. This will allow the clouds to become trapped in an orbit around the black hole.

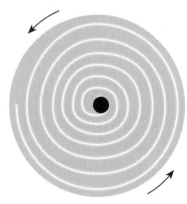

Figure 3.31 A rotating accretion disc; the line shows the spiral infall of one particle.

This result is usually adopted as the 'standard' black hole mass in an AGN. It is some 10^7 times greater than the mass of black holes inferred to exist in binary stars that emit X-rays. Hence, the name *massive black hole* has been adopted.

This Section has deliberately avoided conceptual difficulties associated with black holes. For example, try asking an expert what might happen if you should fall into a black hole! The whole topic of the physics of time and space in the strong gravity surrounding a black hole is fascinating.

3.5.2 An accretion disc

In Subsection 4.5.1 of Book 1, you met the idea of how an accretion disc could form around the more compact star in a binary. Whatever its nature, let us call the AGN engine M. Consider a gas cloud moving to one side of M, like cloud A in Figure 3.30. The gravity of M will cause the gas cloud to accelerate towards it. The cloud will reach its maximum speed when it is at its closest approach to M, but will slow down again as it moves away; it will move away to a distance at least as great as the distance from which it started. Thus far nothing is new; the gas cloud will behave exactly as it would if it came near some other gravitationally attracting object, such as a Sun-like star.

Now, let us extend the argument to a number of gas clouds being accelerated towards M from different directions in space (Figure 3.30). This time, as the gas clouds get to their closest approach they will collide with each other, thus losing some of the kinetic energy they had gained as they fell towards M. Therefore some, but not all, of the clouds of gas will have slowed to a speed at which they cannot retreat, so they will go into an orbit around M, rather like the short-period comets around the Sun. Further collisions amongst the gas clouds will tend to make their orbits circular, and the direction of rotation will be decided by the initial rotation direction of the majority of the gas clouds. The effect of the collisions will be to heat up the gas clouds; the kinetic energy they have lost will have been converted into thermal kinetic energy within each cloud, and so the cloud temperature will rise.

So far, we can envisage a group of warm gas clouds in a circular orbit about M. But the clouds of gas are of a finite size, and the inner parts of the gas clouds will want to orbit M faster than the outer parts. A form of friction (*viscosity*) will act to make the outer parts of the clouds try to slow the rotation of the inner parts. The consequence of this is that the inner parts of the gas clouds will fall inwards to even smaller orbits. This process will continue until a complete **accretion disc** is formed around M (Figure 3.31). If you look at the path of a small part of one gas cloud, you can see that it will spiral in towards M. This process occurs only for a *viscous* gas – planets in the Solar System do not show any tendency to spiral in to the Sun because interplanetary gas is very sparse. The viscosity causes the gas to heat up further, the energy coming from the gravitational attraction of M for the gas. The heating effect will be large for objects with a large gravitational field.

Thus far, the story is the same whether M is a massive black hole or some other object. Black holes have the strongest gravitational fields of any imagined compact object, so will impart the maximum amount of heat to an accretion disc. Once the gas clouds have reached the inner edge of the accretion disc around a black hole, they will encounter the Schwarzschild radius. At this point, they will fall into the black hole. Note that the accretion disc is located *outside* the Schwarzschild radius, so the heat can be radiated away as electromagnetic radiation. The accretion model is of such interest because an accretion disc around a massive black hole can radiate away a vast amount of energy, very much more than a star or a cluster of stars. It is this radiated energy that is believed to constitute the power of an AGN.

You may be wondering how large the accretion disc is; after all, the accretion disc as well as the black hole has to fit inside the AGN. The accretion disc gets hotter and therefore brighter as the Schwarzschild radius is approached. The brightest part is what matters; this is at only three to five times the Schwarzschild radius, so there is no problem of size.

3.5.3 An accreting massive black hole

Detailed calculations, beyond the scope of this Course, but based on the above accretion disc hypothesis, show that if a mass m falls into the black hole, then the amount of energy it can radiate before it finally disappears is about $0.1 \times mc^2$, or about 10% of its rest energy. This is the most efficient process for converting mass into energy ever conceived. A comparable figure for the nuclear fusion of hydrogen in stars is only 0.7% of the rest energy of the four hydrogen nuclei that form the helium nucleus.

ITQ 3.9   How much energy could be obtained from 1 kg of hydrogen (a) if it were to undergo nuclear fusion in the interior of a star, (b) if it were to spiral into a black hole? Would you expect to get more energy if it were to chemically burn in an oxygen atmosphere ?

Now let us apply the idea of an accreting massive black hole to explain the luminosity of an AGN. We have to explain an object of small size and large luminosity. The Schwarzschild radius of a black hole is very small, and the part of the accretion disc that radiates most of the energy will be only a few times this size. As far as the luminosity goes, this will depend on the rate at which matter falls in. Suppose that the matter is falling in at the rate $Q\,\mathrm{kg\,s^{-1}}$. We can now work out the value of Q to produce a luminosity L by writing

$$L = 0.1Qc^2 \text{ or } Q = L/(0.1c^2) \tag{3.6}$$

Using the values $L = 10^{38}\,\mathrm{W}$ (Subsection 3.4.2) and $c = 3 \times 10^8\,\mathrm{m\,s^{-1}}$, we get $Q = 10^{22}\,\mathrm{kg\,s^{-1}}$. Converting this into solar masses per year using $1M_\odot = 2 \times 10^{30}\,\mathrm{kg}$ and 1 year $= 3 \times 10^7\,\mathrm{s}$, we get $Q = 0.2M_\odot$ per year. Is it reasonable that there is a large enough supply of matter for a fraction of a solar mass to be accreted every year? Most astronomers think that the answer is yes, and that even higher accretion rates are plausible – after all our own galaxy has 10–20% of its mass in gaseous form, so there is at least $10^{10}M_\odot$ of gas available.

☐   Does this argument require a massive black hole, or will any black hole such as one of $5M_\odot$ do?

■   The mass of the black hole does not enter into the above calculation.

Moreover, the mass calculated in Subsection 3.5.1 is an upper limit. So, why is a *massive* black hole needed? To see why, we ask: is there any limit to the power L that can be radiated by an accretion disc around a black hole, or can one conceive of an ever-increasing value of L if there is enough matter to increase Q? There *is* a limit to the amount of power that can be produced, and it is called the **Eddington limit**. As the black hole accretes faster and faster, the luminosity L will go up in proportion, that is to say the accretion disc will get brighter and hotter. Light and other forms of electromagnetic radiation exert a pressure on any material they encounter. (This pressure is difficult to observe on Earth because it is difficult to find a bright enough light source.) Around an accreting black hole with a luminosity of 10^{38} W, the radiation will be so bright that it will exert a large outwards pressure on the accreting material. When this pressure exactly counteracts the inward spiralling arising from the black hole's gravity, accretion will cease. This process acts to regulate the luminosity of an accreting black hole.

To work out the Eddington limit, it is necessary to balance radiation pressure against the effects of the black hole's gravity. Consider an atom of gas near the outer edge of the accretion disc. The radiation pressure on it is proportional to L, whereas the inward spiralling is proportional to the mass M of the black hole (assuming the mass of the accretion disc to be negligible). A balance is achieved when L_E = constant $\times M$, where L_E is the Eddington limit. Detailed calculations (well beyond the scope of this Course) give

$$L_E/W = (1.3 \times 10^{31})M/M_\odot \tag{3.7}$$

This is the upper limit of the luminosity of a black hole of mass M – the luminosity can be lower than L_E but not higher. The larger the mass M, the greater the value of L_E.

Putting $L = 10^{38}$ W into Equation 3.7, we find that $M = 7.7 \times 10^6 M_\odot$. So we see that we do need a *massive black hole* to account for the engine in an AGN, and $10^8 M_\odot$ is usually assumed.

In summary, then, the Eddington limit requires an **accreting massive black hole** to have a mass of order $10^8 M_\odot$, the accretion rate is at least a significant fraction of a solar mass per year, and the Schwarzschild radius is about 3×10^{11} m.

3.5.4 Activity in normal and starburst galaxies

You have seen how an accreting black hole may constitute the engine in an AGN. Questions that come to mind are:

- Are massive black holes present only in active galaxies, or are they present in some normal galaxies as well?
- If so, could they be accreting at a reduced rate?
- Are there any side-effects caused by the matter falling in to feed the black hole?

The provisional answers to all these questions appear to be yes. If a galaxy contained a black hole accreting at a reduced rate, you would expect the galaxy to have an active nucleus (variable, broad emission lines) but with a reduced luminosity. Such nuclei have been observed in nearby galaxies, such as the beautiful spiral M81 (Figure 2.5a, Plate 3.12). Several observations of the centre of our own galaxy have suggested that our galaxy may be mildly active (Subsection 1.5.3).

We have shown that the mass accretion rate in an active galaxy needs to be appreciable, several per cent of a solar mass per year. If it is interstellar gas that is sucked in, then it is straightforward to imagine that such motion could give rise to compression waves in the gas, which would in turn give rise to star formation. Hence you might expect active galaxies to show starburst properties. There is now evidence to support this conjecture!

3.5.5 Is there evidence for a massive black hole?

The model for the engine we have discussed so far involves an accreting massive black hole. This lies at the centre of the AGN, which comprises a region of gas, emitting broad spectral lines, an obscuring torus, a forbidden line region, and maybe some jets. The size was deduced from the observed variability. The most rapid variability probably applies to the radiation (typically X-rays) from the accretion disc; the broad line region, forbidden line region and dust torus may well be larger, because the variability of broad lines, forbidden lines and infrared radiation, respectively, is less and less rapid.

If observers were able to get close enough to an AGN, they should be able to resolve the various features of the AGN. They would expect to see the jet (if any) farthest from the centre, then the forbidden line region and any dusty torus, then closer in the broad line region, and then closest of all the hot accretion disc around the black hole. If all these features could be observed in the predicted relative positions and with the predicted spectra, the astronomer could demonstrate that the model is correct. The trouble is that all these features, apart from the outer part of the jet, are far too small to be resolved.

Let's try to estimate the angular size. In Subsection 3.4.1, we made a size estimate of 2.6×10^{13} m for an AGN with a 1 day variability. At a distance of 20 Mpc (6×10^{23} m), this will appear to have an angular size of $2.6 \times 10^{13}/(6 \times 10^{23})$ = 4×10^{-11} radian, or about 10^{-5} arcsec. This is much too small to be resolved. So we conclude that there is no chance of being able to spatially resolve the black hole's accretion disc.

One outstanding feature of the black hole model for the engine is that the black hole must be massive, for reasons argued in Subsection 3.5.3. Can one at least detect the presence of a massive central object? Yes, there is an indirect way to estimate the mass of the central object. In NGC 4151, the nearest Seyfert galaxy with broad lines, the broad lines are observed to vary as well as the continuous spectrum. The line variations lag about 10 days behind associated variations in the continuous spectrum. The usual interpretation is that the variations commence in the engine, this being where the continuous spectrum originates, then take 10 days to 'light up' the broad line region. So the broad line region must be a distance r of about 10 light days from the engine. Supposing that the broad lines are Doppler-broadened by rotation around the engine, then one has a picture of regions of gas moving at a speed v of about 7×10^3 km s^{-1} around a central engine of mass M at a radius r. The value of M can now be calculated from v and r, in the same way that the mass of our galaxy inside radius r was inferred in Chapter 1. Using Equation 1.1,

$$M = rv^2/G$$

with $r = 10$ light days (3×10^{14} m), and $v = 7 \times 10^6$ m s^{-1}, and converting into solar masses, we obtain $M = 10^8 M_\odot$. This is consistent with the value of M for an accreting black hole calculated from consideration of the Eddington limit.

Jets are observed from some AGNs, as described in TV programme 7. They are predicted from the model of the engine as an accreting massive black hole, but their presence does not prove that a black hole is present.

You have now heard the evidence that it really is an accreting massive black hole that provides the engine power for an AGN. Do you think that it is convincing?

ITQ 3.10   How convincing is the scientific evidence for: (a) the existence of accreting massive black holes in AGNs; (b) the occurrence of nuclear fusion in the Sun and other stars; (c) the laws governing the orbits of the planets around the Sun?

$$L_E = (1.3 \times 10^{31}) \times 10^6 M_\odot$$
$$= 1.3 \times 10^{37} M_\odot$$
$$L_E \Rightarrow 1.3 \times 10^{37} \text{ W}$$
$$= 3.38 \times 10^{10} L_\odot$$

Summary of Section 3.5 and SAQs

1   Mass accretion by a massive black hole can plausibly account for the engine in an AGN.

2   The black hole must have a mass of around $10^8 M_\odot$ and must accrete the order of $0.1 M_\odot$ per year.

3   The hypothesis of accreting massive black holes is plausible, but remains unproven.

SAQ 3.9 (Objective 3.9)   Estimate the accretion rate onto a black hole needed to account for the luminosity of a Seyfert nucleus that has twice the luminosity of our galaxy. Express your answer in solar masses per year. What, other than the accretion rate, limits the luminosity?

3.6   Quasars and their uses

In this Section, we shall go into quasars in more detail than in Section 3.3. The description of AGNs in Section 3.4 remains valid, as does the accreting massive black hole model of Section 3.5. We cover:

1   The large redshift of quasars and its normal interpretation;

2   Quasars as the most luminous objects in the Universe;

3   How astronomers can use quasars to detect galaxies that are normally too distant to be seen;

4   How quasars are the stock in trade of the observational cosmologist;

5   How quasar light can be bent by distant galaxies to give us 'double vision'.

Quasars were discovered in the early 1960s. 3C 48 was known as a radio source that was coincident in position in the sky with a star-like visible object. This was new, because up till then most known radio sources were either double-lobed and associated with an elliptical galaxy (the radio galaxies of Subsection 3.3.5) or were objects within our own galaxy. Much more puzzling was the visible wavelength spectrum of this 'star'; instead of being the normal absorption line spectrum of a star, the spectrum showed broad emission lines at wavelengths that were not recognized. At this point the term quasi-stellar object (QSO) or quasar was coined.

The big step forward occurred in 1963, when the Dutch astronomer Maarten Schmidt (1929–) pointed out that the emission lines of 3C 48 could be understood as normal emission lines of hydrogen, oxygen, nitrogen, etc., which had undergone a *large redshift z* given by Equation 2.1, $(\lambda_{obs} - \lambda_{em})/\lambda_{em}$, where λ_{obs} is the observed wavelength and λ_{em} the emitted wavelength. It has since been found that all quasars have emission lines that can be understood in this way, although the redshift is different for each individual quasar. 3C 273 has the smallest redshift, 0.158 (Figure 3.32).

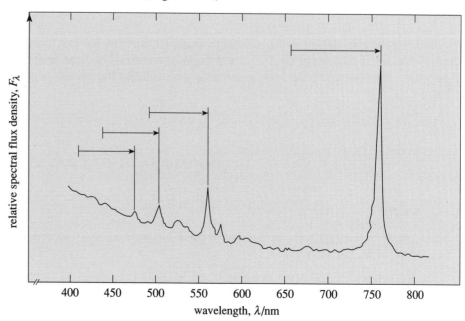

Figure 3.32   The optical spectrum of 3C 273. The arrows show the shift of the lines from their normal wavelengths.

At first, it was thought that the visible image of quasars is purely star-like (just a point of light). Subsequent very careful observations have shown that at least some quasars are surrounded by a faint fuzz, which is probably the light from a normal galaxy – hence the family resemblance between a quasar and a Seyfert galaxy. It seems that the difference is that the AGN or point source is just brighter in the case of a quasar. The broadband spectrum of 3C 273 shows the familiar AGN pattern.

Although the first quasar discovered was a relatively strong radio source, it has subsequently been found that the majority of quasars are not strong radio emitters. Hence the terms **radio loud** and **radio quiet** have come into use: a radio-loud quasar is one that emits strongly in the radio region (Figure 3.33). There are probably real physical differences between radio-loud and radio-quiet quasars, just as there is a difference between radio galaxies and Seyfert galaxies. One idea is that radio-loud quasars, like radio galaxies, reside in elliptical galaxies, whereas radio-quiet quasars, like Seyferts, reside in spiral galaxies. Radio-loud quasars often show jet structures like those of radio galaxies, and these sometimes appear to be moving towards us at very large velocities.

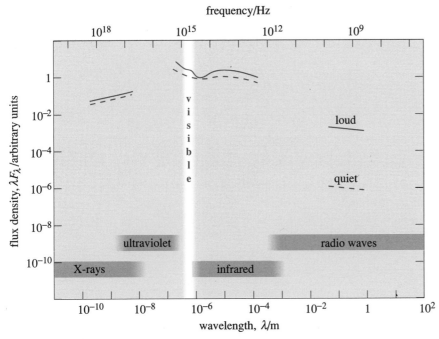

Figure 3.33 Average broadband spectra of radio-loud and radio-quiet quasars. Corrections have been made for the redshift of the sample of quasars.

Like other AGNs, quasars are sources of X-ray, ultraviolet and infrared radiation. Searching for new quasars is a flourishing industry amongst astronomers, who usually pick them out from surveys, and confirm that they really are quasars by checking for redshifted, broad emission lines in their spectra.

3.6.1 Distance, and a controversy

The nearest quasar is 3C 273. Figure 3.32 shows its optical spectrum, and Plate 3.23 its visible appearance. From its redshift, $z = 0.158$, it is possible to estimate roughly the quasar's distance, using the formula for Hubble's law (Equation 2.2):

$$z = H_0 d/c$$

Using $c = 3.00 \times 10^5 \, \text{km s}^{-1}$ and $H_0 = 75 \, \text{km s}^{-1} \, \text{Mpc}^{-1}$, we obtain $d = 630 \, \text{Mpc}$ – a very much larger distance than those of most well known clusters of galaxies.

All other quasars have redshifts larger than 0.158, so their distances are correspondingly greater than that of 3C 273. Many quasars may have redshifts greater than 1.0, and it turns out that, at such large redshifts, the proportionality in Equation 2.2 between z and d no longer holds. Figure 3.34 gives a measure of distance for large values of z, though apart from the general upward curvature, the degree of deviation from a straight line is very poorly known. Distances of objects at large values of z are discussed in Book 4. For the purposes of this chapter, it is necessary to remember only this: the larger the value of z, the greater the distance.

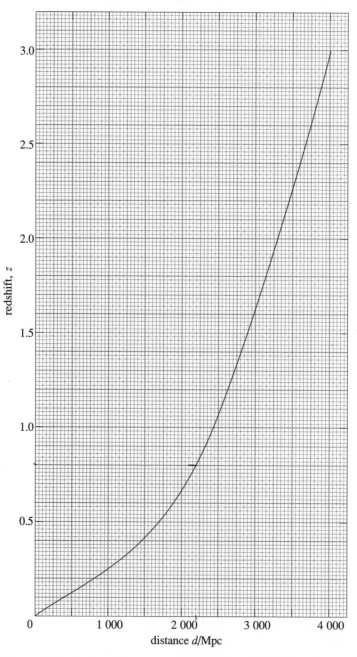

Figure 3.34   A plot of distance versus redshift, with Hubble's constant $H_0 = 75 \, \mathrm{km \, s^{-1} \, Mpc^{-1}}$. Apart from the general upward curvature, the degree of variation from a straight line is very poorly known.

Now for the controversy. In the above two paragraphs it has been assumed, through our use of Hubble's law, that the redshift is caused by the expansion of the Universe. Others have proposed that the redshift could be caused by some other mechanism, such as gravitational redshift (which can be observed in the spectra of white dwarfs). If one accepts this, then the consequence that quasars lie at great distances no longer follows. A minority of astronomers have taken this view, and to support their opinion have pointed out that quasars appear to lie in positions close to nearby galaxies. Although these views are not generally accepted, they are seriously argued and should not be dismissed in too cavalier a fashion. Having said that, we shall proceed with the conventional view that quasars have large redshifts caused by great distances.

Quasars as luminous active galaxies

Quasars are bright enough to be seen in optical telescopes, yet from their redshifts they lie at distances considerably greater than those at which normal galaxies can be detected. Hence in the optical the quasars *must* be more luminous than normal galaxies. Also quasars, like other AGNs, have a broadband spectrum in which a good part of their luminosity lies at other wavelengths, making them even more luminous than normal galaxies.

ITQ 3.11 A quasar with a redshift $z = 0.2$ appears as bright in the optical as a normal galaxy with a redshift $z = 0.02$. How much more luminous is the quasar than the galaxy, if it is found that only 10% of the quasar's emission is at optical wavelengths?

3.6.2 Use of quasars to probe distant galaxies

When the optical spectrum of a quasar is examined in detail, a host of absorption lines is seen in addition to the strong and broad emission lines. These lines can be identified with gaseous absorption lines for which the redshift is large, but is always smaller than the redshift of the quasar. These absorption lines are attributed to galaxies in the line of sight to the quasar, as in Figure 3.35. Normally, absorption lines are present at a range of discrete redshifts caused presumably by a number of galaxies at different distances, and therefore with different redshifts.

It is easier to 'see' very distant galaxies by examining the absorption lines in the spectrum of a quasar, than it is to see very distant galaxies on direct images. This is because the farther away the galaxies, the fainter their starlight. But if a galaxy absorbs light from a quasar, its absorption lines will show up provided the quasar is bright enough.

The absorption lines in the spectrum of a quasar are frequently referred to as the **Lyman alpha forest** (Figure 3.36). The Lyman alpha part of the name refers to an absorption line of atomic hydrogen. 'Forestry' has become an industry amongst astronomers!

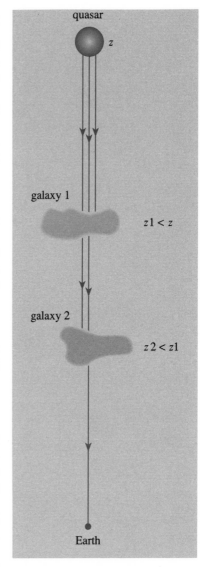

Figure 3.35 Schematic diagram showing intervening galaxies in line of sight to a quasar. Galaxy 2 will have the smallest redshift.

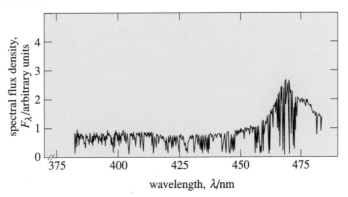

Figure 3.36 The Lyman alpha forest in the spectrum of a quasar. Note that the wavelength range is quite small.

123

ITQ 3.12   Would you expect the galaxies giving rise to the absorption lines in Figure 3.36 to be elliptical, lenticular, spiral or irregular ?

3.6.3   *Probing the Universe*

As you should now realize, quasars are the most distant astronomical objects that can be studied. Being so distant, the radiation they emit has taken a very long time to reach us, and this time is comparable with the age of the Universe. The **lookback time** depends on the redshift of the quasar, as shown in Figure 3.37. Therefore, by studying quasars, one can study the Universe when it was young. The great distance and the long lookback time make quasars one of the main tools of cosmology, which is dealt with in Book 4.

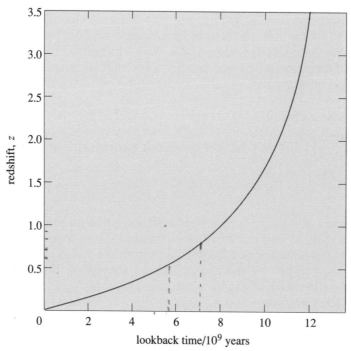

Figure 3.37   Redshifts of quasars and the corresponding lookback times, with Hubble's constant $H_0 = 75\,\mathrm{km\,s^{-1}\,Mpc^{-1}}$. Apart from the general upward curvature, the degree of variation from a straight line is very poorly known (and in this version is not the same at large z as that in Figure 3.34).

One simple fact you should be aware of without embarking on your study of cosmology — quasars are more abundant at great distances than they are nearby. This means that, in the early Universe, quasars were more abundant than they are at present. So quasars must die out as time proceeds. This may be true for other AGNs, but there is very little evidence.

ITQ 3.13   How far away would a quasar with a redshift $z = 1.0$ lie, and what would be the lookback time?

3.6.4   *Gravitational lenses*

The 'double quasar' is an interesting phenomenon. Two quasars are seen close together in the sky; they have similar spectra with similar redshifts, and their variabilities are correlated. It is as if the one quasar is being seen twice. This can be understood as the gravitational effect of an intervening galaxy: the light from a single quasar is bent by the gravity of the galaxy, so that two images are seen. The galaxy is behaving rather like a lens, and this effect is called **gravitational lensing** (Figure 3.38).

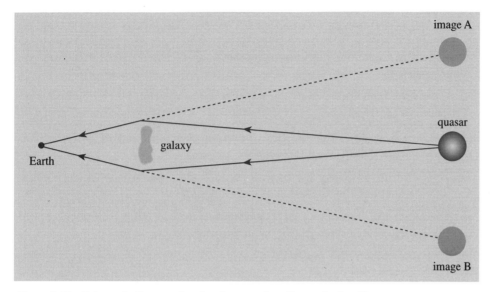

Figure 3.38　Schematic diagram showing the operation of a gravitational lens.

The bending of light by the gravity of a massive object is an example of an effect explained by General Relativity, as is the gravitational redshift produced close to a massive object, such as a white dwarf or a black hole. Gravitational lensing may in due course be used as a basis for measuring the mass distribution of a galaxy or galaxy cluster that bends the radiation from a background quasar.

Observations of gravitational lensing support the assumption that quasars lie at great distances, because the quasar must lie behind the lensing galaxy. Unfortunately, not much is known about the intervening galaxies that are responsible for the lensing.

Summary of Section 3.6 and SAQs

1　Quasars have very large redshifts.

2　It is generally accepted that the redshifts are related to distance via Hubble's law, in which case quasars must be very distant and highly luminous.

3　Quasars can show up intervening galaxies; these galaxies leave telltale absorption lines.

4　Quasars are the most distant objects that can be seen, and therefore we see them as they were when the Universe was young. Hence they are used to probe the early Universe.

5　The light from quasars can be bent by intervening galaxies acting as gravitational lenses.

SAQ 3.10 (Objectives 3.4 and 3.10)　Suppose that a quasar has a redshift of 0.2, and appears as bright in the optical as a galaxy like our own at a distance of 200 Mpc. Estimate its optical luminosity as a multiple of that of the galaxy.

SAQ 3.11 (Objective 3.10)   Suppose that a quasar has a redshift of 0.30. Its spectrum shows evidence for absorption lines at $z = 0.27$ and at $z = 0.23$. What objects, and at what distances, give rise to the absorption lines ?

Objectives for Chapter 3

After studying Chapter 3 (and any associated audio, video or TV material), you should be able to:

3.1   Give brief definitions of the terms, concepts and principles listed at the end of the Objectives.

3.2   Explain how and why the line spectrum of a starburst or active galaxy differs from that of a normal galaxy.

3.3   Explain how and why the overall (broadband) spectrum of a starburst or active galaxy differs from that of a normal galaxy.

3.4   Calculate the luminosity of a starburst or active galaxy in terms of the luminosity of a normal galaxy, such as our own.

3.5   Describe briefly the observed features of starburst galaxies and the four main classes of active galaxies (Seyfert galaxies, quasars, radio galaxies and BL Lac objects).

3.6   Understand the evidence that indicates the presence of a compact active galactic nucleus (AGN) in each class of active galaxies.

3.7   Calculate the upper limit to the size of an AGN.

3.8   Explain why an AGN should emit broad lines, forbidden lines and continuous radiation.

3.9   Give an account of an accreting massive black hole as the probable engine of an AGN, and relate its luminosity to its accretion rate.

3.10 Describe the observed properties of quasars, calculate their distances from their redshift, and explain how they can be used to probe the intervening space.

List of scientific terms, concepts and principles used in Chapter 3

Term	Page	Term	Page	Term	Page
accreting massive black hole	118	forbidden line region	112	quasar	104
accretion disc	116	gravitational lensing	125	radio galaxy	105
active galactic nucleus (AGN)	89	HII region	90	radio-loud quasar	121
active galaxy	89	inverse square law	110	radio-quiet quasar	121
BL Lac object	107	jet	106	Schwarzschild radius	115
broad line region (BLR)	112	λF_λ	97	Seyfert galaxy	102
broadband spectrum	91	line broadening	92	spectral excess	98
Doppler broadening	92	lookback time	124	starburst galaxy	89
Eddington limit	117	Lyman alpha forest	123		
engine	89	massive black hole	115		
forbidden line	92	overall spectrum	91		

Chapter 4
Galaxies in space

Prepared for the Course Team by Barrie W. Jones

Contents

4.1   Introduction

So far in Book 3, we have concentrated on individual galaxies. In this final chapter, you will see how they are distributed in space and learn a bit about how they move through space.

To determine how the galaxies are distributed in space we need to measure the directions and distances to as many galaxies as possible. We can then prepare a three-dimensional map. In the main, the distances are obtained by first measuring the redshift of the spectral lines in each galaxy's spectrum, and then applying Hubble's law (Subsection 2.3.5). This provides a relatively rapid way of obtaining the distances to lots of galaxies. Even so, covering just a small part of the observable Universe takes an enormous amount of time, even on large telescopes. This is because most galaxies are distant and consequently faint, and the flux densities are so low that even with the best equipment it takes a long time to obtain a spectrum. Therefore, astronomers also prepare two-dimensional maps, by measuring just directions, without distances. Some three-dimensional information can still be inferred, by setting up a three-dimensional model and using it to construct a two-dimensional map. The broad features of this constructed map are then compared with the actual map, and the model is adjusted to improve the agreement. Video sequence 11 contains some details of how the maps are made, and you should watch it after you have read this chapter.

Why do we want to map the spatial distribution of the galaxies? One reason is to satisfy our curiosity about what our surroundings are like, in this case on the largest scale of all. Another reason is to test cosmological theories, that is theories of the origin and large-scale evolution of the Universe. Such tests are hard won, and so this really is a crucial reason for mapping, making it one of the most important current endeavours in astronomy. The maps provide a test because cosmological theories have to explain the large-scale distribution of matter. They have to explain why the galaxies are not scattered randomly through space, but are organized into the sorts of vast structure that you will meet shortly.

The galactic maps actually show the spatial distribution of luminous matter, which is certainly baryonic. This adds nothing *directly* to our understanding of the nature and distribution of *dark* matter, which accounts for at least 90% of the mass in and around galaxies and which seems to consist largely of non-baryonic matter (Subsections 1.2.1, 2.4.2 and 2.5.1). However, in our cosmological theories, the spatial distributions of non-baryonic matter and baryonic matter are intimately related, and so a map of luminous baryonic matter does provide a powerful test of the theories.

In this chapter we offer you a brief introduction to the maps, and an even briefer account of how they are used to test cosmological theories. We start with the Local Group of galaxies – our own backyard, if you can imagine a backyard about 2 million parsecs across! We then look at some other clusters, and then at the Local Supercluster, of which the Local Group is a very small part. We then consider the largest structures so far detected. The chapter ends with a very brief consideration of the large-scale motions of the galaxies.

4.2   The spatial distribution of galaxies

4.2.1   Clusters

It could have been the case that the galaxies are distributed uniformly through space, with equal distances between them. Mapping shows that this is not so. It could also have been the case that the galaxies are distributed randomly through space. Mapping again shows that this is not so. Let's start in our own neighbourhood, where we see that there is a concentration. Figure 4.1 shows the main members of the **Local Group** of galaxies. The whole group consists of over 30 galaxies, occupying a volume of space about 2 million parsecs across (2 Mpc, about 6 million light years). This is to be compared with a distance of about 0.03 Mpc across the disc of the Milky Way.

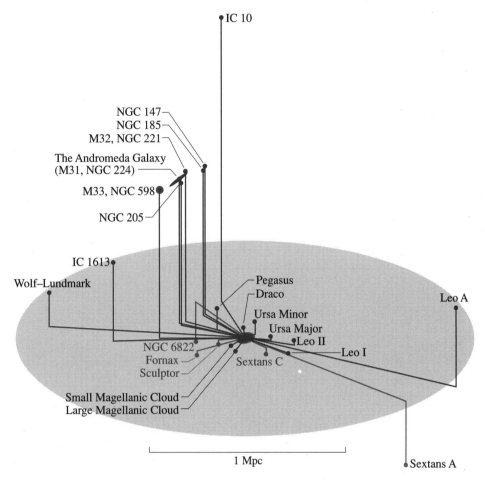

Figure 4.1   The main members of the Local Group of galaxies. Some are named after the constellations in whose directions they lie.

The Local Group is probably not a transitory bunching of galaxies but is bound together by gravity, so that each member moves in an orbit determined by the gravitational fields of the other members. Its most massive members are our own Milky Way, and another spiral galaxy, the Andromeda Galaxy (M31, Plate 3.8b), which is slightly more massive than ours. Of the remaining galaxies, the most massive are our near neighbours the irregular Large and Small Magellanic Clouds (Plate 3.10b and c), and the more distant spiral M33, each being of order ten times less massive than ours.

Most of the remaining members are dwarf elliptical galaxies (Plate 3.9b and c), so faint that they are still being discovered! The final table in *Images of the Cosmos* lists most of the galaxies in the Local Group.

A concentration of galaxies is called a **cluster**. The Local Group is thus a cluster, though it contains a rather small number of members. Indeed, some astronomers regard it as little more than a binary galaxy, consisting of the Milky Way and the Andromeda Galaxy, plus a handful of minor attendants.

There are many clusters, and they are somewhat arbitrarily divided into two main categories: sparse clusters contain up to about a thousand members; rich clusters contain more than about a thousand members. Within the sparse clusters there is a sub-category, called a group, with up to about 50 members. The Local Group is a sparse cluster, and also a group. The clusters do not differ very greatly in volume, and therefore the galaxies in a rich cluster are far more tightly packed than in a group. Nearly all galaxies seem to belong to a cluster of some sort.

One of the nearest clusters beyond the Local Group is about 3 Mpc away, in the direction of the constellations Ursa Major and Camelopardalis. It is a group centred on the large spiral M81 (Plate 3.12), and is called simply the M81 Group, or the Ursa Major–Camelopardalis Group. Another member is the spiral M82 (Plate 3.17). There are a lot of clusters in our cosmic neighbourhood, and Figure 4.2 shows their spatial distribution. The spheres represent the volumes of each cluster, and the shaded plane is an extension of that in Figure 4.1. All of these are sparse clusters.

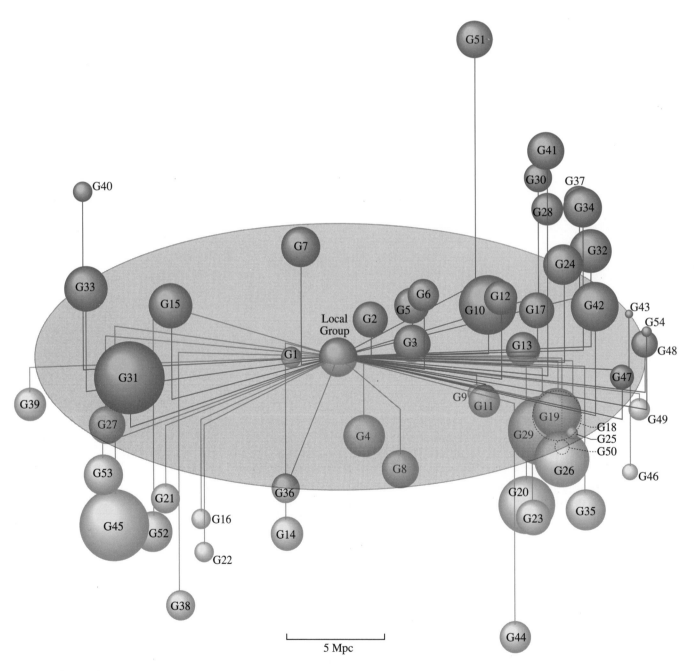

Figure 4.2   The spatial distribution of nearby clusters of galaxies (all are sparse clusters). The G numbers are cluster catalogue numbers. G2 is the M81 Group.

We have to look farther away for rich clusters. The nearest is in the direction of the constellation of Virgo, and is called (unsurprisingly) the Virgo Cluster (Plate 3.30). It is about 20 Mpc away, about 3 Mpc across (typical of clusters), and contains about 2 500 galaxies, including the giant elliptical M87 (Plate 3.21). The colour plates include images of galaxies from other clusters too.

Clusters also differ in the relative numbers of the different sorts of galaxy that they contain. For example, the Virgo Cluster and the Hercules Cluster are rich in spiral galaxies, whereas the Coma Cluster is rich in ellipticals. There is little understanding of the reasons for such differences.

ITQ 4.1 Discuss whether the galaxies are uniformly distributed through space on a scale of 1 Mpc.

The answer to ITQ 4.1 highlights an important issue – on what scale does the Universe look uniform? Clearly not on the scale of 1 Mpc. What happens when we look at a larger scale?

4.2.2 Superclusters

It could have been that *clusters* of galaxies are distributed randomly through space – mapping again disabuses us of this notion. Since the mid 1970s we have realized that clusters are concentrated into **superclusters**, of which there are very many.

Figure 4.3 shows the **Local Supercluster**. It is 25 to 50 Mpc across (typical of superclusters) and is centred on the Virgo Cluster (Figure 4.3), which accounts for about 20% of the 1 000 or so *bright* galaxies in the Local Supercluster. The number of faint galaxies is far greater. The position of the Local Group is marked in Figure 4.3, and you can see that it is an outlying member of the Local Supercluster, at the extremity of a lobe-shape that consists of many clusters. In Figure 4.2 this extremity encompasses the large number of clusters of galaxies in the *right* half of the figure – the viewpoints differ between the two figures. In Figure 4.2 the lobe-shape would extend to the right. The Virgo Cluster also lies to the right in Figure 4.2 (a long way off!), its centre lying in an extension of the shaded plane.

With superclusters, have we now come to the largest scale structure in the Universe?

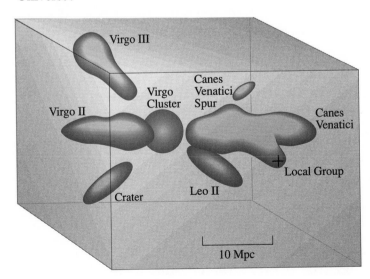

4.2.3 The large-scale spatial distribution

When we look out to distances much greater than the size of the Local Supercluster, we have rather few means of measuring distances.

☐ Which means are still available?

■ From Figure 2.9 we see that, much beyond about 50 Mpc, we have only supernovae, brightest cluster galaxy, and Hubble's law.

In fact, for measurements of large numbers of individual galaxies, Hubble's law is at present the best method. This means that, for large-scale surveys, astronomers obtain redshifts, which are then converted into distances using Hubble's law (Equation 2.2).

ITQ 4.2 A galaxy in the Coma Cluster, which lies in a neighbouring supercluster, has a redshift of 0.023. Calculate the upper and lower limits for the distance to this galaxy, expressing your answer in megaparsecs.

Because we still do not know Hubble's constant H_0 to within about a factor of two, we shall adopt the common convention of quoting distances that correspond to a selected value. Our selected value, as in earlier chapters, and as in *Images of the Cosmos,* is 75 km s^{-1} Mpc^{-1}. The distance to the galaxy in ITQ 4.2 is then about 100 Mpc.

In April 1990, a team of astronomers from Oxford University published a survey of the positions of about two million galaxies around the south *galactic* pole, over an area covering about 10% of the celestial sphere. The outcome of this two-dimensional survey is shown in Plate 3.29. Though individual redshifts were not measured, the more distant galaxies surveyed are at a redshift of nearly 0.20, corresponding to distances approaching 800 Mpc if $H_0 = 75$ km s^{-1} Mpc^{-1}. Statistical tests show that in this survey the distribution of galaxies across the sky is distinctly non-random. The picture is consistent with the existence of clusters and superclusters. Most importantly, the survey provides evidence that galaxies are concentrated into winding filaments and curved sheets, with huge voids that are largely empty of galaxies. Within the filaments and sheets the superclusters lie, although there are also many galaxies outside superclusters. This filament/sheet/void geometry is quite different from that of roughly spherical superclusters randomly distributed in space – the visible Universe is more like a sponge. In this survey, only on a scale of order 60 Mpc or larger does the distribution of galaxies across the sky begin to become uniform.

Various other surveys have been made, including several that are three dimensional. Plates 3.32 and 3.33 show the outcome of a survey carried out during the 1980s and 1990s by astronomers at the Harvard-Smithsonian Centre for Astrophysics (CfA). This survey, and others, confirm the sponge-like distribution of the galaxies, with voids up to about 60 Mpc across. They have also revealed other structures considerably larger than 60 Mpc. Of particular note is the existence of 'walls' of galaxies. One such is the Great Wall, visible in Plate 3.33. This covers an area at least 200 Mpc by 80 Mpc, but is probably only about 6 Mpc thick. It is thought to be composed of the galaxies in the sheets surrounding several adjacent voids.

The caption to Plate 3.33 gives a smaller estimate of the size of the Great Wall. The larger size here is preferred.

The CfA survey extends out to about 200 Mpc, the same order of size as the largest structures it has revealed. Other surveys have probed much farther, by concentrating on narrow ranges of angle: this is rather like investigating the Earth's structure by examining the core extracted from a borehole. Figure 4.4 shows the outcome of one such **'borehole' survey** carried out by astronomers in the UK (University of Durham) and in the USA (University of California, Santa Cruz). This survey extends to about 2 000 Mpc towards the north and south galactic poles.

☐   Why were these particular directions selected?

■   Obscuration by dust in the plane of our galaxy is minimized.

The 'borehole' surveys show what could be other walls, spaced by about 150 Mpc. This might mean that voids exist with these vast sizes, though it is possible that interleaving walls have not been detected. It is also possible that many of the 'walls' that are present in Figure 4.4 are not walls at all but clusters of galaxies that happened to lie in the path of the 'borehole'.

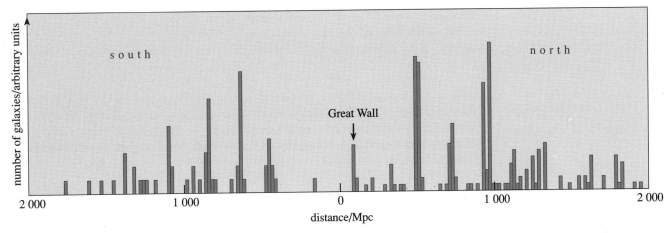

Figure 4.4   A 'borehole' survey, possibly revealing walls of galaxies.

Walls, with dimensions of at least 200 Mpc, are among the largest structures so far discovered. We cannot rule out the possibility of the discovery of yet larger structures, when three-dimensional surveys that cover larger volumes are completed. However, it must be borne in mind that some large structures, such as filaments, though clear to the eye, do not necessarily represent very strong concentrations of galaxies. There is some evidence that at the largest scales yet surveyed the spatial distribution of galaxies is fairly uniform.

We thus live in exciting times: we do not know the scale of the largest structures in the Universe, as far as the spatial distribution of the galaxies is concerned. We need to probe farther out, covering the whole sky. Indeed, there's a lot of space still to explore: the edge of the observable Universe, a notion to be explained in Block 4, has been approached only in the few really deep 'borehole' surveys, so only a small range of angles has so far been covered to any great distance.

Summary of Section 4.2 and SAQs

1   An important reason for mapping the spatial distribution of galaxies is to test cosmological theories.

2   Galaxies tend to group into clusters, of order 3 Mpc across, probably gravitationally bound. Clusters differ in the numbers of members, and in the relative abundances of spiral and elliptical galaxies.

3   Clusters tend to group into superclusters, of order 50 Mpc across.

4   Clusters, superclusters and individual galaxies tend to lie in filaments and sheets, enclosing voids up to at least 60 Mpc across. Walls, with dimensions of at least 200 Mpc, have been identified, and there might be yet larger structures: as yet only a small fraction of the observable Universe has been mapped.

SAQ 4.1 (Objective 4.2)   Calculate how long it takes light to travel across the Local Group. Hence comment on the statement that 'Figure 4.1 shows the Local Group as we see it today'.

SAQ 4.2 (Objective 4.2)   Accepting a figure of 15 billion years for the age of the Universe (Block 4), calculate the fraction of this age at which we see today (i) the Virgo cluster and (ii) the farthest reach of the CfA survey.

SAQ 4.3 (Objective 4.2)   In a two-dimensional survey of the sky, about a thousand galaxies lie within an area of about a square degree, whereas in the surrounding area of the sky the density is significantly less. Why can one not necessarily conclude that all one thousand or so galaxies belong to a single rich cluster?

SAQ 4.4 (Objective 4.2)   Suppose that you are to make a model of the spatial distribution of the galaxies by pouring ball-bearings of various sizes into a jar. (a) What, in the real Universe, is represented by (i) the ball-bearings, (ii) the air around them, and (iii) the diameter of the average ball-bearing? (b) List the main shortcomings of this model.

4.3   Cosmological implications

In Section 4.1, I told you that the spatial distribution of galaxies helps us to test cosmological theories. At the very largest scale the theories assume that the Universe is homogeneous, that is each large volume of space looks the same as any other. Galaxy surveys indicate that this might be the case, though it is still possible that more extensive surveys will reveal inhomogeneity. Cosmology on these largest scales is the subject of Block 4, and I'll say no more about it here. Instead, let's consider the departures from homogeneity that clearly occur on smaller scales, as apparent in clusters, superclusters and the larger structures – the cosmological theories have to explain these too.

In Subsection 2.5.1 you met the Big Bang, and I shall assume, along with almost every other astronomer in the world, that the Universe did indeed start with a Big Bang – more on this in Block 4. What is at issue here is whether the density fluctuations that were present in the cosmic gas at the earliest times could have led to the large-scale structure. The remarkable conclusion, borne out by detailed analysis, is that the luminous baryonic matter that we see today could not alone have given rise to the large-scale structure. Something else is required.

There is a lot of evidence that there is plenty of something else around – dark matter (Subsections 1.2.1 and 2.4.2). Unfortunately, the maps of large-scale structure don't reveal where it is; but the maps do help cosmologists to construct theoretical models of its distribution, and in most models it is more uniformly distributed – less clumped – than the luminous baryonic matter that we see as the galaxies. *Cold* dark matter is one possibility – you met this stuff in Subsection 2.5.1 as a possible medium for aiding the formation of galaxies. Can it also explain the large-scale structure? It seems not, or at least not on its own. This is a major conclusion from the surveys of the spatial distribution of galaxies. One possible explanation of the large-scale structure requires cold dark matter mixed with a small proportion of *hot* dark matter. **Hot dark matter**, like cold dark matter, would be extremely hard to detect except via its gravitational effects, but unlike cold dark matter it has a large amount of thermal kinetic energy, and so is less easily gathered up by gravitational attraction.

One form of hot dark matter that has been suggested is energetic (hot) neutrinos, assuming that the neutrinos have non-zero mass. We know only that neutrinos have at most an extremely small mass – far less than the electron mass – and many scientists believe the neutrino mass to be truly zero. Nevertheless, even a tiny mass will do, and the possibility of a tiny mass cannot be ruled out.

This and other possible explanations of the large-scale structure are mentioned in video sequence 11, which you should watch at the end of this chapter.

Clearly, it is of cosmological importance to know where the dark matter is. Is there any prospect of mapping its spatial distribution?

☐ How do we know it exists?

■ From its gravitational effects in galaxies (Subsection 1.2.2) and in clusters of galaxies (Subsection 2.4.2).

In the next Section, I shall outline attempts to use its gravitational effects to map its distribution on the largest scales.

4.4   Large-scale motions

In Subsection 2.3.5 a warning was sounded about interpreting galactic redshifts as Doppler shifts. Though a proper interpretation must await Block 4, we must point out here that a galactic redshift is a direct result of the increasing distance between us and the galaxy – the galaxy is receding from us, and the greater the rate of recession the greater the redshift.

We must, however, take care to distinguish between two components of a galaxy's motion. The first component is that which we would obtain if, *independent of Hubble's law*, we somehow measured the distance d to a galaxy, and we then obtained its redshift z from Hubble's law

$$z = (H_0/c)d \tag{2.2}$$

The redshift corresponds to a certain rate of recession, which is thus determined. Note that the value of z and the rate of recession associated with z are average values for the distance d. This component of motion is often called the **Hubble flow**. It follows from Hubble's law that the greater the distance, the greater the average rate of recession.

The actual value of z for an individual galaxy would not necessarily be exactly the same as that obtained from Equation 2.2, and this is because of the second component of a galaxy's motion, the motion peculiar to itself, called the **peculiar motion**. This could be in any direction with respect to us, but if there is a component of its peculiar motion towards us then its redshift will be reduced, and if it is away from us its redshift will be increased. For all but the closest galaxies, the Hubble flow is far larger than any peculiar motion.

Large-scale motions are peculiar motions that are coordinated, so that one or more clusters or superclusters are moving as a whole with respect to the Hubble flow. The importance of large-scale motions is that they help us to identify mass concentrations, baryonic or otherwise: clusters and superclusters are attracted towards such concentrations. They also help us to distinguish between competing models of the composition of dark matter.

The Local Group is moving at about $600 \, \text{km s}^{-1}$ with respect to the Hubble flow. (This is only 0.2% of the speed of light, not very fast in cosmological terms, but it does mean that the Local Group is not *quite* at rest with regard to the cosmological reference frame defined by the Hubble flow. Within the Local Group, the Galaxy is moving towards the Andromeda Galaxy at $40 \, \text{km s}^{-1}$, the Sun orbits the Galactic centre at $230 \, \text{km s}^{-1}$, and the Earth orbits the Sun at $30 \, \text{km s}^{-1}$.)

This large-scale motion of the Local Group has been measured from observations of the microwave background radiation that pervades the Universe, as will be described in Block 4. For other galaxies, the procedure is statistical in that it involves many galaxies at a time. It is also complicated and so the details will not concern us, though it is important to note that the large-scale motions for these other galaxies are uncertain in most cases.

The uncertainty in the motions has given rise to a debate about the existence of the so-called Great Attractor in our cosmic neighbourhood − an enormous, slab-like concentration of mass rather less than half-way between us and the Great Wall (Figure 4.4), greatly exceeding the mass inferred for that region from the observed galaxies. The Great Attractor could account for much of the peculiar motion of the Local Group and the Local Supercluster. If it exists, then galaxies obscured by the Milky Way could account for its mass − we would not *have* to invoke dark matter.

The existence of the Great Attractor was proposed on the basis of calculations that showed that galaxies on this side of its location have a peculiar motion towards it, and that galaxies on the far side *also* have a peculiar motion towards it. The Great Attractor was held to account for nearly all of the peculiar motions of the clusters and superclusters that it influenced, including that of the Local Group. However, other calculations have shown that the galaxies on the far side of the Great Attractor have peculiar motions *away* from it, thus denying the Great Attractor's existence! Yet other calculations suggest that the peculiar motions can be accounted for by the attraction of the known clusters of galaxies.

The resolution to this problem lies in more comprehensive surveys of the spatial distribution of the galaxies, and of their peculiar motions. Such surveys will give us a much clearer idea of the distribution through space of all forms of matter, dark matter as well as luminous baryonic matter. We will then be able to conduct better tests of our theories of cosmology.

Preliminary results (March 1994) of a survey of galaxy motions over the entire sky out to new record distances of over 160 Mpc, made in the USA and Chile, indicate that regions of the Universe as large as 300 Mpc across might be drifting with respect to the larger Universe. If this result is upheld, then the Universe will be seen to have structure on a scale rather larger than that indicated near the end of Subsection 4.2.3; keep your eye on the S281 *Yearbook*!

Summary of Section 4.3 and 4.4 and SAQs

1   The spatial distribution of the galaxies tends to become homogeneous on the very largest scales surveyed; cosmological theories assume large-scale homogeneity.

2   Clusters, superclusters and larger scale structures cannot be explained in cosmological theories based on the Big Bang, unless some agency has been operating in addition to the luminous baryonic matter that we see today. Cold dark matter alone is an insufficient agent.

3   The motion of a galaxy consists of its participation in the Hubble flow, and its own peculiar motion. For all but the closest galaxies, the Hubble flow is by far the larger component.

4   Large-scale motions are coordinated peculiar motions.

5   The importance of large-scale motions is that they help us to map the complete mass distribution in the Universe, including dark matter. At present, however, the motions are difficult to determine accurately.

SAQ 4.5 (Objective 4.3)   What is the effect of the large-scale motion of the Local Group on the redshifts of galaxies at a given, large distance from us, in various directions?

You should now watch video sequence 11, Galaxies in space, *and then video sequence 12,* Interacting galaxies. *Remember to read the associated notes first.*

Conclusion

You have now reached the end of Block 3, *Galaxies*, in which we have described our own galaxy, the Milky Way, and the various other types of galaxy, including active galaxies. We concluded by considering the spatial distribution of the galaxies, up to the largest scale currently achieved. We also considered large-scale motions of the galaxies. You are now ready to address one of the biggest issues of all – the origin and large-scale evolution of the Universe. This is the subject of Block 4, the final Block in the Course, and in spite of the size of the issue, it is the smallest Block!

Objectives for Chapter 4

After studying Chapter 4 (and any associated audio, video or TV material), you should be able to:

4.1   Give brief definitions of the terms, concepts and principles listed at the end of the Objectives.

4.2   Describe the spatial distribution of the galaxies, on scales from clusters, to superclusters, and to yet larger scales.

4.3   Give a very brief account of the large-scale motions of the galaxies.

4.4   Outline how cosmological theories can be tested using the spatial distribution of galaxies and the large-scale motions.

List of scientific terms, concepts, and principles used in Chapter 4

Term	Page	Term	Page
borehole survey	132	Local Group	129
cluster of galaxies	129	Local Supercluster	131
hot dark matter	134	peculiar motion	135
Hubble flow	135	supercluster	131
large-scale motion	135		

ITQ answers and comments for Chapter 1

ITQ 1.1

As stars age they convert light elements into heavier elements. Some of the heavier elements thus produced may be released into the interstellar medium by various processes, particularly through supernova explosions. Because of this the interstellar medium is evolving chemically, gradually becoming richer in heavy elements. Thus, stars that formed a long time ago are expected, on average, to have a lower abundance of heavy elements than stars that formed more recently, i.e. the metallicity of old stars is expected, broadly speaking, to be less than that of young stars.

ITQ 1.2

(a) $M(r)/r = k$, so Equation 1.2 becomes $v = (Gk)^{1/2}$. In other words, v does not change with radius and the rotation curve is flat, as shown in Figure 1.34a.

(b) The volume of a sphere enclosed within a radius r is equal to $\frac{4}{3}\pi r^3$, so $M(r) = k\frac{4}{3}\pi r^3$. Equation 1.2 then becomes $v = (Gk\frac{4}{3}\pi r^3/r)^{1/2} = r(Gk\frac{4}{3}\pi)^{1/2}$; thus v increases with increasing r, and the rotation curve is as shown in Figure 1.34b.

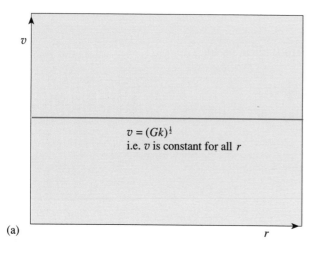

$v = (Gk)^{\frac{1}{2}}$
i.e. v is constant for all r

(a)

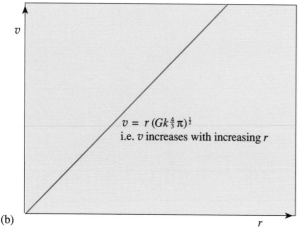

$v = r(Gk\frac{4}{3}\pi)^{\frac{1}{2}}$
i.e. v increases with increasing r

(b)

Figure 1.34   Answer to ITQ 1.2.

ITQ 1.3

Gould's belt is inclined at about 20° to the Galactic plane. This can be deduced from the observation that, in Figure 1.14, 20° is the greatest angular departure from the Galactic plane. [*Comment*: Figure 1.35, which shows Gould's belt and the Galactic plane as great circles on the celestial sphere, may help you to understand this answer. Note that the figure is centred on the Sun.]

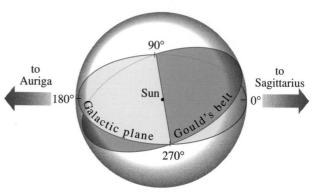

Figure 1.35   For use with answer to ITQ 1.3.

ITQ 1.4

(a) Following the method of SAQ 1.5, the radius of the orbit of the inner end of the imagined spiral arm (in km) is

$$2\pi \times 4 \times 3.09 \times 10^{16}\,\text{km} = 7.77 \times 10^{17}\,\text{km}$$

A rotation speed of $220\,\text{km s}^{-1}$ may be expressed, rather unconventionally, as $6.95 \times 10^9\,\text{km yr}^{-1}$ (because 1 yr = 3.16×10^7 s). Thus, the time required to execute one orbit is

$$\frac{7.77 \times 10^{17}}{6.95 \times 10^9}\,\text{yr} = 1.12 \times 10^8\,\text{yr}$$

So, over a period of 5×10^9 years the inner end of the arm will have executed about $(5 \times 10^9)/(1.12 \times 10^8)$ orbits, i.e. about 45 orbits.

(b) Similarly, the outer end of the arm, which follows an orbit of circumference $1.94 \times 10^{18}\,\text{km}$, will have completed about $(45 \times 7.77/19.4)$ orbits, i.e. about 18 orbits.

(c) Thinking of the spiral arm as something like a piece of chewing gum stretching between the inner and outer end points, it seems clear that over 5×10^9 years the arm will have wound itself around the centre of the Galaxy many times. Whereas the real arms (so far as they have been observed) seem to wind about half-way round the Galaxy, the arms imagined in this question would wind round the Galaxy about $(45 - 18) = 27$ times! Clearly, this is very different from what is observed.

ITQ 1.5

Since the spiral density wave rotates 'rigidly', maintaining its shape, its rotation curve must be a straight line passing through the origin just like that of a rigid wheel (Figure

1.9). To fix the slope of the line we need to know the rotational speed at just one (non-zero) distance from the centre. Since we know that the density wave and the disc co-rotate at 15 kpc from the centre, we can find the value we need from Figure 1.11 – it is about 235 km s^{-1}. The resulting rotation curve for the density wave is shown in Figure 1.36.

In Figure 1.11 it is assumed that the Sun is at 8.5 kpc from the Galactic centre and that its rotation speed is 220 km s^{-1}. From Figure 1.36, the rotation speed of the density wave at this radial distance is 133 km s^{-1}. So the speed of approach, by the Sun, should be about (220 – 133) km s^{-1} = 87 km s^{-1}.

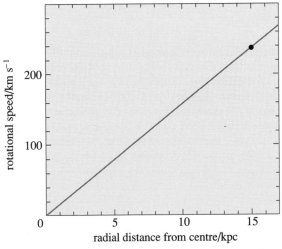

Figure 1.36   For answer to ITQ 1.5.

ITQ 1.6

10^9 years is considerably longer than the time required for matter in the disc to orbit the Galactic centre (see ITQ 1.4 answer). If all open clusters lived for this length of time, they *would* be distributed evenly throughout the disc. However, given the much shorter lifetime of the smaller clusters they will not survive long enough to become evenly distributed. [*Comment*: It should be noted that references to the lifetime of the cluster relate to the period of time for which the cluster itself is an identifiable entity; they do not refer to the lifetimes of the individual stars making up the cluster. Many of the stars will continue to survive long after the cluster has ceased to exist. Indeed, it is widely thought that the Sun itself may once have been a member of an open cluster, though this is little more than a hypothesis, based on the idea that stars form in clusters.]

ITQ 1.7

Main sequence stars convert hydrogen into helium in their cores. The *main sequence turn-off point* occurs at about the time they exhaust the hydrogen in their cores. *Subgiant stars* are converting hydrogen into helium in a shell surrounding the core. *Red giant stars* are also converting hydrogen into helium in a shell, and will have begun to convert the helium in their cores into heavier elements such as carbon. [*Comment*: Figure 1.23 also shows the *horizontal branch*. Over much of this branch the stars are also converting helium into heavier elements in their cores while continuing to burn hydrogen in a shell surrounding the core.]

ITQ 1.8

The angular separation θ between two points at a common distance d is related to the physical distance l between the two points by the formula

$l \approx d(\theta/\text{radians})$
(see *Preparatory science,* mathematical appendix)

provided that $(\theta/\text{radians})$ is small. Thus, at $d = 8.5$ kpc we get the following correspondences (remembering that 360° = 2π radians):

$1° (= 1.75 \times 10^{-2} \text{ radians}) \equiv 150 \text{ pc}$

$1 \text{ arcmin} (= 2.91 \times 10^{-4} \text{ radians}) \equiv 2.5 \text{ pc}$

$1 \text{ arcsec} (= 4.85 \times 10^{-6} \text{ radians}) \equiv 0.041 \text{ pc}$

[*Comment*: So, even if Baade's window allowed us to see objects at a distance of 8.5 kpc, they would still be about 600 pc from the Galactic centre.]

ITQ answers and comments for Chapter 2

ITQ 2.1

High-mass main sequence stars, open clusters, HII regions and an abundance of population I stars (relative to population II stars), are all symptoms of continuing star formation. Since new stars are unlikely to be formed in the absence of gas – the raw material needed to make them – it is to be expected that each of the named types of object will increase or become more significant in going from ellipticals (which have little gas) to spirals, which are actively forming stars in their discs. [*Comment*: This is indeed the case.]

ITQ 2.2

Figure 2.28 shows an edge-on view of the ring. The time taken by light to cover the distance from point A to point B is 340 days. Consequently the distance, d, from A to B is

$$d = (3.00 \times 10^8 \text{ m s}^{-1}) \times (340 \times 24 \times 60 \times 60 \text{ s})$$
$$= 8.81 \times 10^{15} \text{ m}$$

Now, this distance is related to the diameter of the ring, CA, and the angle of inclination, 43°, by the formula

$$d = \text{CA} \sin 43°$$

Therefore

$$CA = \frac{d}{\sin 43°} = \frac{8.81 \times 10^{15}\,\text{m}}{0.682}$$
$$= 1.29 \times 10^{16}\,\text{m}$$

[Comment: The figures used in this ITQ were based on observations made by the International Ultraviolet Explorer satellite and by the Hubble Space Telescope. The observed angular diameter of the ring is 1.66 arcsec, which, with the above value of CA, yields a distance of 52 kpc for the LMC. This distance of the ring is thought to be within about 5% of the true distance. Previously the uncertainty in the distance of the LMC was about 12%.]

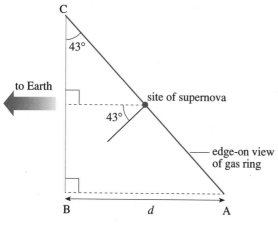

Figure 2.28   For answer to ITQ 2.2.

ITQ 2.3

(a) Flux density F, luminosity L and distance d are related by the equation:

$$F = L/(4\pi d^2) \qquad \text{(Book 1, Equation 2.8)}$$

and so

$$d = [L/(4\pi F)]^{1/2} \qquad \text{(Book 1, Equation 2.9)}$$

(b) The value of d given by the formula is an upper limit because it makes no allowance for the possibility that some of the radiation emitted by the source might be absorbed between the point of emission and the point of detection. Interstellar matter, interplanetary matter in the Solar System and absorption in the Earth's atmosphere are all possible causes of an unaccounted reduction in F that would lead to an overestimate of d.

ITQ 2.4

For a Cepheid with a period of 10 days, Figure 2.11 shows that the maximum absolute visual magnitude M_V is −3.5. [Comment: Note that the data in Figure 2.11 are for type I (classical) Cepheids.]

ITQ 2.5

The following items of information are needed:
(i) The observed flux density from each supernova. [Comment: In practice this would be limited to particular wavebands.]

(ii) A value for the distance, d, to each host galaxy. [Comment: In principle this might be based on observations of Cepheid variable periods, but in practice the distances used in these particular cases were based on other bright star observations.]

(iii) An estimate of the amount of radiation absorbed or scattered between the supernova and the flux detector. [Comment: Again, in practice this would be limited to a particular waveband.]

The observed flux density should be increased by the amount that was lost due to scattering and absorption, and the resulting total, F, used in conjunction with the distance, d, to find the luminosity, L, where (ITQ 2.3):

$$L = 4\pi d^2 F$$

[Comment: If F had been limited to some particular band of wavelengths then L would be limited in the same way. In practice, the calibration of the Type Ia supernova method uses other information besides the three nearby examples mentioned in the question. For example, a number of Type Ia supernovae have been observed in the Virgo cluster of galaxies. Despite the uncertainties about the distance of the Virgo cluster, these observations have been used in the calibration.]

ITQ 2.6

Unlike variable stars, planetary nebulae only need to be observed once, and unlike supernovae they are long-lived and relatively numerous.

ITQ 2.7

The method provides insight only into the mass within the largest value of r for which the rotation curve has been measured. [Comment: If you don't remember the details, review Subsection 1.2.5.]

ITQ 2.8

As in young open clusters, the luminosity of a youthful population is usually dominated by the luminous blue stars at the upper end of the main sequence. [Comment: Note that not all young stars are blue − main sequence blue stars evolve more rapidly than red stars, so an old collection of stars will have a larger proportion of red ones. Note also that the references to the 'blueness' of stars and galaxies, made here and elsewhere, must be treated with care. Remember, owing to the operation of the eye, all stars appear to be more-or-less white with just slight tinges of colour, depending on their temperature. Nonetheless, hot stars are 'blue' and cooler stars 'red' in the sense that their spectra contain greater or lesser proportions of the wavelengths corresponding to these colours. Astronomers, who use the term 'colour' in a technical sense when referring to stars and galaxies, will often describe an object as blue or red even though it may appear to be some shade of white (or even an entirely different colour) when seen or photographed.]

ITQ 2.9

As the stars all grow older together the massive blue stars would exhaust their core hydrogen first and leave the main sequence. They would then become progressively redder and soon disappear by way of a supernova. As this process continues, stars of lower and lower mass would gradually leave the main sequence, evolve through the giant stage and eventually end their lives as white dwarfs. The overall effect would be to reduce the luminosity of the galaxy (because of the growing predominance of lower main sequence stars) and to make it redder. [*Comment*: However, within this general development there are many subtleties that must be considered, mainly arising from the complicated evolution of luminosity and colour of each individual star or type of star. If your recollection of stellar evolution is hazy it would probably be a good idea to look again at Figures 3.16 and 3.23 in Book 1 before continuing.]

ITQ 2.10

Apart from supernovae, all the other processes (outlined in Book 1) that cause stars to expel matter might be of relevance: stellar winds, the formation of planetary nebulae, novae, and perhaps even stellar flares and coronal mass ejections. [*Comment*: In addition, the interaction of high-energy cosmic rays with various nuclei already present in the ISM may lead to further chemical evolution via a process known as spallation (see Book 2, Subsection 8.3.4).]

ITQ answers and comments for Chapter 3

ITQ 3.1

From the absorption spectrum of a star you can find the chemical composition, surface temperature and luminosity by examining the strengths and widths of the absorption lines. By looking for Doppler shifts on the lines, you can measure radial velocity and, if the Doppler shifts occur periodically, you can observe the binary nature of stars. [*Comment*: Emission lines are occasionally seen, usually from gas clouds around the star.]

ITQ 3.2

Our galaxy is rotating at between 200 and 250 km s^{-1} (Figure 1.11). Edge-on, this is the approach speed at one extremity and the recessional speed at the other. So the line-width that would be observed if the Galaxy were viewed edge-on is 400–500 km s^{-1}.

ITQ 3.3

Dust has not been mentioned because it does not emit at optical wavelengths. [*Comment*: It does *absorb* such wavelengths, its effect being to dim the continuum and lines from the stars and HII regions. As you will see as you study this chapter, dust does radiate significantly, but only at far infrared wavelengths.]

ITQ 3.4

(a) X-rays are emitted by X-ray binary stars and supernova remnants. (b) Infrared radiation comes predominantly from cool stars, dust clouds, dust in HII regions, and the centre of the galaxy. (c) Radio wavelengths are emitted by HII regions, supernova remnants, atomic hydrogen, molecular hydrogen and other molecules. [*Comment*: If you got one or two in each waveband, that's fine.]

ITQ 3.5

In the radio wave region, $\lambda = 10^5 \, \mu\text{m}$ so $\lambda F_\lambda = 10^5 \, \mu\text{m} \times 10^{-28} \, \text{W m}^{-2} \mu\text{m}^{-1} = 10^{-23} \, \text{W m}^{-2}$. In the far infrared region $\lambda = 100 \, \mu\text{m}$ so that $\lambda F_\lambda = 100 \, \mu\text{m} \times 10^{-23} \, \text{W m}^{-2} \mu\text{m}^{-1} = 10^{-21} \, \text{W m}^{-2}$. In the X-ray region, $\lambda = 10^{-4} \, \mu\text{m}$ so $\lambda F_\lambda = 10^{-4} \, \mu\text{m} \times 10^{-20} \, \text{W m}^{-2} \mu\text{m}^{-1} = 10^{-24} \, \text{W m}^{-2}$. The largest of these λF_λ values is $10^{-21} \, \text{W m}^{-2}$, so we conclude that the far infrared dominates.

ITQ 3.6

For galaxy A in the optical region, $\lambda = 0.5 \, \mu\text{m}$ and $F_\lambda = 10^{-29} \, \text{W m}^{-2} \mu\text{m}^{-1}$ so $\lambda F_\lambda = 0.5 \times 10^{-29} \, \text{W m}^{-2}$. For galaxy B in the optical, $\lambda F_\lambda = 0.5 \times 10^{-30} \, \text{W m}^{-2}$. For galaxy B in the far infrared, $\lambda = 100 \, \mu\text{m}$ and $F_\lambda = 10^{-30} \, \text{W m}^{-2} \mu\text{m}^{-1}$ so $\lambda F_\lambda = 10^{-28} \, \text{W m}^{-2}$. So, on the basis of the data, galaxy B is the more luminous galaxy.

ITQ 3.7

An angular size limit of 0.1 arcsec can be expressed as 5×10^{-7} radian. Multiplying this by the distance shows that the upper limit on the size $= 50 \times 10^6 \times 5 \times 10^{-7} \, \text{pc} = 25 \, \text{pc}$. The upper limit from the variability is $2R = ct = (3 \times 10^8 \, \text{m s}^{-1}) \times (6 \times 10^5 \, \text{s}) = 1.8 \times 10^{14} \, \text{m} = 0.006 \, \text{pc}$.

ITQ 3.8

If the AGN is at twice the distance but appears as bright as the normal galaxy in the optical, then by the inverse square law it must be emitting four times the optical light of the normal galaxy like our own. If only one-fifth of the AGN's energy is emitted in the optical, then its luminosity is $4 \times 5 = 20$ times that of the normal galaxy like our own, assuming that (as usual) the normal galaxy emits mostly at optical wavelengths. The AGN luminosity is thus about $20 \times 2 \times 10^{10} L_\odot = 4 \times 10^{11} L_\odot$.

ITQ 3.9

A mass of 1 kg of hydrogen has a rest energy of mc^2. If this mass of hydrogen were to undergo nuclear fusion to produce helium, the energy liberated would be 0.007 of its rest energy: $E = 0.007mc^2 = 0.007 \times 1 \times (3 \times 10^8)^2 \, \text{J} = 6 \times 10^{14} \, \text{J}$. If 1 kg of hydrogen were to fall into a black hole, the energy liberated would be approximately $0.1mc^2 = 0.1 \times 1 \times (3 \times 10^8)^2 \, \text{J} = 9 \times 10^{15} \, \text{J}$. You would expect much *less* energy from the chemical reaction.

ITQ 3.10

(a) An accreting massive black hole is a hypothesis that has been thought up to account for AGNs. There is really no *conclusive* evidence to support the hypothesis. [*Comment*: However, no-one has a *better* idea of how to produce enough power for an AGN in the small volume.] (b) The occurrence of nuclear fusion in the Sun was originally a hypothesis proposed to explain the Sun's energy source. The whole theory of the structure and evolution of stars of different mass and different composition has been based on the nuclear fusion idea. The agreement of this theory with observations is strong confirmation that the nuclear fusion idea is correct. (c) The laws governing the motion of the planets round the Sun account for all planetary motions ever observed and allow future motions to be predicted. This is the strongest evidence for their correctness. [*Comment*: It could even be said that people have conducted experiments by launching spacecraft that are found to move according to these same laws.]

ITQ 3.11

From Equation 2.2, the ratio of the distances is the same as the ratio of the redshifts, that is 0.2/0.02. If the two appear at the same brightness, then by the inverse square law, the quasar is $(0.2/0.02)^2 = 100$ times as bright. Allowing for the fact that 90% of the quasar's energy is emitted at other wavelengths, we find that the quasar is roughly $10 \times 100 = 1\,000$ times as luminous as the galaxy. [*Comment*: Effects of redshift on the broadband spectrum have been ignored. Also, note from Figure 3.34 that, at $z = 0.2$, we can still use Equation 2.2.]

ITQ 3.12

The galaxies giving rise to the absorption lines must contain a good deal of gas to produce the absorption lines. Spiral and irregular galaxies contain such gas, but not elliptical or lenticular galaxies.

ITQ 3.13

For a rough estimate of the distance of a quasar, use the graph in Figure 3.34. You should read off a value of about 2 400 Mpc. To find the lookback time, use the graph Figure 3.37. You should read off a value of about 8×10^9 years. [*Comment*: These values are for $H_0 = 75$ km s^{-1} Mpc^{-1}.]

ITQ answers and comments for Chapter 4

ITQ 4.1

The Local Group is a concentration of galaxies about 2 Mpc across. The nearest other cluster is about 3 Mpc away. Therefore, at least in our neighbourhood, the galaxies are *not* uniformly distributed through space on a scale of 1 Mpc. [*Comment*: In this respect, our neighbourhood is typical.]

ITQ 4.2

Rearranging Hubble's law (Equation 2.2), we get

$$d = z(c/H_0)$$

Thus, using the lower value of 50 km s^{-1} Mpc^{-1} for Hubble's constant (Subsection 2.3.5), we get

$$d = 0.023(3.0 \times 10^5 \text{ km s}^{-1})/(50 \text{ km s}^{-1} \text{ Mpc}^{-1})$$

$$= 138 \text{ Mpc}$$

(140 Mpc to two significant figures.)

Using the higher value of 100 km s^{-1} Mpc^{-1} for Hubble's constant, we get half this value: 70 Mpc.

SAQ answers and comments for Chapter 1

SAQ 1.1

On the basis of Figures 1.6 and 1.7, together with the information in Table 1.1, it is clear that most of the hydrogen (by mass) is in the form of atoms and molecules. The atomic hydrogen is distributed fairly uniformly throughout the disc, where much of it is in the form of a warm intercloud medium and diffuse clouds. The density of atomic hydrogen falls off steeply within the bulge, as distance from the Galactic centre decreases.

Molecular hydrogen is almost as common as atomic hydrogen though its detailed distribution is quite different. In the disc, it is mainly concentrated within the Sun's orbit and there is a sharp peak in the distribution at a distance of about 4 kpc from the Galactic centre. It occurs mainly in dense and diffuse clouds. [*Comment*: The molecular hydrogen around 4 kpc is mainly in the form of giant dense clouds.]

Ionized hydrogen is rarer than molecular hydrogen, though its distribution within the disc shows the same kind of peaked distribution. It is mainly found in the HII regions and in warm and hot intercloud media. More ionized hydrogen is found in the hot but tenuous intercloud medium that permeates the halo.

SAQ 1.2

The area of the ring is $\pi(R_2{}^2 - R_1{}^2)$ where R_2 is the outer radius and R_1 the inner radius. Thus, in this case, the area is

$$\pi\left[(4.4\,\text{kpc})^2 - (4.2\,\text{kpc})^2\right] = 5.40\,\text{kpc}^2 = 5.40 \times 10^6\,\text{pc}^2$$

Now, according to Figure 1.7 the column densities of molecular, atomic and ionic hydrogen between 4.2 and 4.4 kpc are, respectively, $5.5 M_\odot\,\text{pc}^{-2}$, $4.5 M_\odot\,\text{pc}^{-2}$ and $4.5 M_\odot\,\text{pc}^{-2}$. Thus the total mass of hydrogen in the ring is

$$5.40 \times 10^6 \times (5.5 + 4.5 + 4.5)M_\odot = 7.8 \times 10^7 M_\odot$$

Since helium accounts for roughly 25% of the mass of the ISM, and hydrogen for the other 75%, it follows that the total mass of helium accompanying this mass of hydrogen will be approximately

$$\frac{25}{75} \times 7.8 \times 10^7 M_\odot = 2.6 \times 10^7 M_\odot$$

[*Comment*: Note that no use has been made of the thickness of the ISM. This piece of information had, in effect, already been taken into account in producing Figure 1.7. It wasn't needed in this calculation but you shouldn't forget its implicit presence.]

SAQ 1.3

High-velocity stars are not part of the disc population (population I); they really belong to the halo population (population II). As members of this older population they would naturally be expected to have, on average, lower metallicity than the Sun.

SAQ 1.4

Cosmic rays are charged particles, and so will be deflected by magnetic fields as they travel through the Galaxy. Since the Milky Way certainly includes a magnetic field, it follows that if cosmic rays do originate in supernovae they are unlikely to be found coming from the directions of such supernovae. Rather, they will 'bounce around' inside the Milky Way as they are deflected from one region to another.

SAQ 1.5

According to Figure 1.11, a star at a distance of 8.5 kpc from the Galactic centre will have a rotation speed of $220\,\text{km s}^{-1}$. The circumference of a circular orbit of radius 8.5 kpc is

$$2\pi \times 8.5 \times 10^3 \times 3.09 \times 10^{16}\,\text{m} = 1.65 \times 10^{18}\,\text{km}$$

Thus, the time required for a star, such as the Sun, to execute such an orbit is

$$\frac{1.65 \times 10^{18}\,\text{km}}{220\,\text{km s}^{-1}} = 7.50 \times 10^{15}\,\text{s}$$

Now, there are $3.16 \times 10^7\,\text{s}$ in one year. So the time required for one complete orbit by the Sun is

$$\frac{7.50 \times 10^{15}}{3.16 \times 10^7}\,\text{years} = 2.37 \times 10^8\,\text{years}$$

Assuming that the Sun has existed for 5.0×10^9 years it follows that the number of orbits will have been

$$\frac{5.0 \times 10^9}{2.37 \times 10^8} = 21$$

Thus there will have been 21 orbits.

[*Comment*: Of course, the two-figure 'precision' in this calculation is largely spurious. Given all the uncertainties that arise in such a grandiose calculation, we should not place any great confidence in such precise figures.]

SAQ 1.6

The disc has a diameter of about 30 kpc, which corresponds to a radius of about 15 kpc. Thus the area of the disc is $\pi(15\,\text{kpc})^2$ and, since it is 1 kpc thick, its volume is $\pi(15)^2\,\text{kpc}^3$. By similar reasoning, the optically observable volume of the disc is $\pi(5)^2\,\text{kpc}^2 \times 1\,\text{kpc} = \pi(5)^2\,\text{kpc}^3$. Thus the fraction of the disc's volume that can be observed is

$$\frac{\pi(5)^2}{\pi(15)^2} = \frac{25\pi}{225\pi} = \frac{1}{9}$$

This limitation is mainly the result of dust in the plane of the Galaxy. [*Comment*: The value of the observable fraction is thus independent of the value assumed for the thickness.]

SAQ 1.7

The Sun is thought to be about 5×10^9 years old. This is older than all but a very few of the longest-lived open clusters. Thus, even if the Sun was originally part of an open cluster it would have long since escaped from the cluster. Possible causes of the escape are gravitational disruption (possibly through an encounter with a giant molecular cloud complex), the 'evaporation' of the cluster, or simply the dispersive effect of differential rotation over a long period of time.

SAQ 1.8

In the density wave theory, the spiral pattern moves round rigidly with an unchanging shape, and does not wind up. Matter in the Milky Way revolves differentially, with a longer period for matter at a greater distance from the Galactic centre. Such matter passes into the spiral arms and then out again. Thus the matter highlighting the spiral arms at any time is not permanently present within the arms and thus the arms have no tendency to wind up.

SAQ 1.9

Tracers of spiral arms include:

- Open clusters
- OB associations
- Bright HII regions
- Dense clouds
- Clouds of neutral hydrogen.

SAQ 1.10

The open clusters would be represented by numerous (~200) dots or small regions mainly clustered around the Galactic plane (zero Galactic latitude). Only a few very nearby clusters would be far from this plane (high Galactic latitude) and even this would be an effect of perspective.

SAQ 1.11

This could be the H–R diagram of a young open cluster. It has a full main sequence and even some suggestion that at the lower end of the main sequence, where stars take somewhat longer to settle onto the main sequence, some are still in the process of establishing themselves. [*Comment*: In fact, Figure 1.24a was loosely based on the H–R diagram of the young cluster NGC 2264 (Plate 1.22a) which is thought to be just a few million years old.]

SAQ 1.12

Orange–white. The brightest stars in a globular cluster will be those at the highest point on the H–R diagram. In the globular cluster H–R diagrams shown in this chapter it is always the case that the stars in this position are cool red giants, i.e orange–white in colour (see Book 1, Chapter 2). [*Comment*: The brightest stars in globular clusters are sometimes used to determine the distances of globular clusters. This was certainly the case in Shapley's original work. As far as possible he made use of variables whose absolute magnitude could be determined by observing the period of their luminosity variation. However, in many cases the clusters were too distant for variables to be observed. In several of these cases Shapley used the brightest stars in the cluster, which he assumed to be of essentially the same brightness in each cluster.]

SAQ 1.13

Most of the atomic hydrogen (H) and molecular hydrogen (H_2) in the Milky Way is found in the disc, apart from the high-velocity clouds of atomic hydrogen that are found in the halo. Hot ionized hydrogen (H^+) is found in both the disc of the Milky Way (in HII regions, and in the hot intercloud medium) and the halo (where it is very thin, and is known as the gaseous corona).

SAQ 1.14

From Figure 1.33, the mass enclosed in a spherical volume of radius 1 pc appears to be of order $4 \times 10^6 M_\odot$. If all this mass is assumed to be in the form of $10 M_\odot$ stars, it follows that the spherical volume must contain about 4×10^5 such stars. Thus, the volume per star is

$$\frac{1}{4 \times 10^5} \times \left(\frac{4}{3} \times \pi \times 1 \, \mathrm{pc}^3 \right) \approx 10^{-5} \, \mathrm{pc}^3$$

Supposing that each of these individual stellar volumes is a small cube within the total spherical volume, with each star at the centre of its cube, it follows that the average separation between neighbouring stars will be about $(10^{-5} \, \mathrm{pc}^3)^{1/3}$, i.e. about 2×10^{-2} pc. [*Comment*: Even a supergiant's radius is only about 10^{-5} pc, so there's plenty of space.]

SAQ 1.15

The radiation might be expected to come from material falling into the black hole, probably from an accretion disc (Book 1, Subsections 4.4.4 and 4.5.1). The basic source of the emitted energy is the release of gravitational energy of the infalling matter. [*Comment*: Perhaps the most important point to note is that the emitted energy is *not* expected to come from *within* the black hole. Such emission is forbidden according to classical physics. Rather, the energy comes from the accretion disc *surrounding* the black hole.]

SAQ answers and comments for Chapter 2

SAQ 2.1

The flattening factor for an elliptical galaxy is $f = (a - b)/a$. For the ellipse shown in Figure 2.3, a is 24 mm and b is 14 mm, so

$$f = \frac{24 \, \mathrm{mm} - 14 \, \mathrm{mm}}{24 \, \mathrm{mm}} = 0.42$$

In assigning a Hubble type to an elliptical galaxy, the number that follows the E is the nearest integer to $10 \times f$. So in this case the appropriate Hubble type would be E4.

SAQ 2.2

(a) NGC 7479 has wide-flung arms, and there is a bar across its centre; it is an SBc galaxy.

(b) M101 also has wide-flung arms and a relatively small bulge; it is a spiral galaxy of type Sc.

(c) NGC 4449 has no symmetry; it is an irregular galaxy.

SAQ 2.3

The ellipsoid is the only three-dimensional shape that presents an elliptical outline to all observers, irrespective of the direction from which it is observed. Oblate and prolate spheroids (and triaxial ellipsoids) are special cases of the general ellipsoid.

SAQ 2.4

The completed Table 2.1 is given on the next page.

Property	Ellipticals	Spirals	Irregulars
approximate proportion of all galaxies	$\gtrsim 60\%$	$\lesssim 30\%$	$\lesssim 15\%$
mass ratio of gas to stars	small, 1% say	5–15%	15–25%
stellar populations	population II	populations I and II	populations I and II
approximate mass range	$\sim 10^5 M_\odot$ to $\gtrsim 10^{13} M_\odot$	$\sim 10^9 M_\odot$ to a few times $10^{12} M_\odot$	roughly $10^7 M_\odot$ to $10^{10} M_\odot$
approximate luminosity range	a few times $10^5 L_\odot$ to about $10^{11} L_\odot$	about $10^9 L_\odot$ to a few times $10^{11} L_\odot$	roughly $10^7 L_\odot$ to $10^{10} L_\odot$
approximate diameter range ^{a}	$(0.01–5)d_{MW}$	$(0.02–1.5)d_{MW}$	$(0.05–0.25)d_{MW}$
angular momentum per unit mass	low	high	low

$^a d_{MW}$ = diameter of Milky Way.

[*Comment*: It is important to realize that many of the properties in the table are difficult to determine and that approximate figures are often poorly determined.]

SAQ 2.5

(a) From Figure 2.10, the period, i.e. the separation between successive peaks, is 5.5 days.

(b) It follows from Figure 2.11 that the peak absolute visual magnitude of δ Cephei is about −3.0.

[*Comment*: Note the logarithmic scale for period in Figure 2.11.]

SAQ 2.6

Shortcomings of the standard candle methods include:

(i) The difficulty of selecting classes of objects or bodies that have a definite luminosity (i.e. standard candles).

(ii) The difficulty of determining the luminosity of those standard candles, i.e. the calibration problem.

(iii) The likelihood that the standard candles, whatever they may be, will simply be too faint to be seen at all in the more distant galaxies.

(iv) The problems associated with the absorption and/or scattering of radiation along the pathway between the source and the detector. These effects generally reduce the flux density received from the source and make it seem farther away than it really is (see ITQ 2.3b).

(v) The possibility, particularly in the case of spirals, that it may be necessary to take into account the orientation of the galaxy relative to the observer (for example, when using the Tully–Fisher method)

[*Comment*: It is also possible that standard candles observed at great distances (and hence at earlier times, because of the finite speed of light) may not be the same as those relatively nearby objects used for calibration.]

SAQ 2.7

(a) Since each datum point corresponds to a *cluster* of galaxies, the distances would have been determined using the brightest cluster galaxy method.

(b) Although Figure 2.16 indicates a reasonably precise value for the distance of each galaxy (up to a redshift of around 0.1), this is illusory – it must be remembered that calibration difficulties make those distances rather uncertain. Thus, the entire distance scale shown on the horizontal axis may well need substantial correction. Such a change would, of course, lead to a revision of any value of Hubble's constant based on Figure 2.16.

SAQ 2.8

See Figure 2.29. [*Comment*: The boundaries between the variously coloured regions of Plate 3.9b are isophotal contours.]

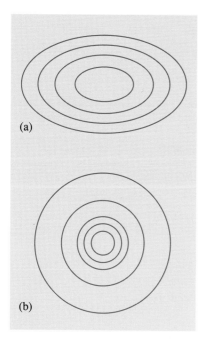

Figure 2.29 The answer to SAQ 2.8: (a) an E4 galaxy; (b) a face-on S0 galaxy.

SAQ 2.9

Stars in elliptical galaxies are moving randomly, unlike the fairly orderly rotation of matter in spirals, so there is little net rotation. Moreover, the lack of significant amounts of gas in ellipticals prevents the use of 21 cm techniques to trace the rotation. On the other hand, the velocity dispersion method can be applied only to galaxies in which the dominant velocities are random. In a spiral galaxy, the dominant motion is *not* random so the virial theorem is not applicable. [*Comment*: Despite the difficulties, some information concerning the rotation of elliptical galaxies has been obtained. However, the rotation is slight and the information sparse compared with that available for spirals.]

SAQ 2.10

(a) M31 is a spiral galaxy, like the Milky Way. Therefore it is to be expected that the nuclear bulge will mainly consist of population II stars whereas the disc will be dominated by population I stars. Since these populations are significantly different, it makes sense to model them separately.

(b) In an E2 galaxy, where there is little or no active star formation, the stars will be mainly long-lived types of the sort common in population II. Thus, lower main sequence stars (i) and red giants (ii) should be well represented, whereas upper main sequence stars (iii) and Cepheid variables (iv) will be rare.

SAQ 2.11

The correct sequence is (c), (a), (b). In Figure 2.27c, all the stars have formed and the main sequence is well populated, though massive blue stars are much less common than low-mass red stars. A few million years later (Figure 2.27a) the very massive blue stars have burnt themselves out and some of the slightly less massive stars have already left the main sequences and started to become cooler, though no less luminous. Overall, by this stage there will have been some reduction in luminosity and a definite change towards a yellower integrated spectrum. After billions of years (Figure 2.27b) even intermediate-mass stars will have started leaving the main sequence and will be entering their giant phase. Overall, owing to the exhaustion of the more massive stars, there will have been a further lowering of luminosity and a movement towards a redder spectrum.

SAQ 2.12

Clearly, if the observations are to be consistent with the theory, the oldest observed stars must have been enriched in some way or, more probably, the matter from which they formed must have already been enriched before their formation took place. One explanation is that the very first stars that formed in galaxies, which would have been unusual stars because of their extremely low metallicities, included many very massive stars that evolved very quickly and soon blew up. This would have enriched the ISM at an early stage, ensuring that all subsequent generations of stars had a metallicity that was well above that of the primordial cosmic gas. [*Comment*: This is the usual explanation. Another proposal, made some years ago, is that there was a particular class of massive stellar objects, usually called population III, that came into existence even before the galaxies had formed. The explosion of these objects would have ensured that the medium from which galaxies condensed was 'pre-enriched'.]

SAQ answers and comments for Chapter 3

SAQ 3.1

For the gas motion use Equation 3.1, $\Delta\lambda/\lambda = \Delta v/c$, where Δv is the magnitude of the velocity range. Then $\Delta\lambda/\lambda = 2\,\text{nm}/654.3\,\text{nm} \simeq 0.003$. Thus the overall spread of internal speeds is $\Delta v \simeq 0.003 \times c \simeq 1\,000\,\text{km s}^{-1}$, which is too large for a normal galaxy.

SAQ 3.2

The wavelengths λ are $0.5\,\mu\text{m}$, $5\,\mu\text{m}$ and $50\,\mu\text{m}$, respectively, therefore the λF_λ values are $5 \times 10^{-28}\,\text{W m}^{-2}$, $5 \times 10^{-28}\,\text{W m}^{-2}$ and $5 \times 10^{-27}\,\text{W m}^{-2}$, respectively. The largest of these values is $5 \times 10^{-27}\,\text{W m}^{-2}$, so the dominant flux is at $50\,\mu\text{m}$, which is in the far infrared. The object is likely to be either a starburst galaxy or an active galaxy.

SAQ 3.3

If the galaxy is active, one would expect to see strong emission lines in the optical, and spectral excesses at non-optical wavelengths. [*Comment* (looking ahead to Sections 3.3 and 3.4): The radiation from an active galaxy should be variable, and this is usually most pronounced at X-ray wavelengths.]

SAQ 3.4

If the object is a starburst galaxy at least as far away as 10 Mpc, its spectral lines should show a redshift equal to or greater than $750 \, \text{km s}^{-1}$ (assuming $H_0 = 75 \, \text{km s}^{-1} \, \text{Mpc}^{-1}$). If it were an object inside our galaxy, its Doppler shift would be smaller than the $200\text{–}250 \, \text{km s}^{-1}$ rotation speed of the Galaxy. So the simplest approach to decide would be to measure the Doppler shift.

SAQ 3.5

Type of galaxy	Emission lines	Intermediate or broad emission lines	Far infrared excess	Strong X-ray emission	Variability	Point-like
starburst	yes	no	yes	no	no	no
active	yes	yes (except BL Lac)	yes (except some BL Lac)	some cases	yes	yes

SAQ 3.6

The limit on the size of the AGN is the limit on the angular diameter in radians, multiplied by the distance. So the limit is $(0.2 \times 5 \times 10^{-6}) \times (20 \times 10^6) \, \text{pc} = 20 \, \text{pc}$. To express this in AU, we need first to convert into metres using $1 \, \text{pc} = 3 \times 10^{16} \, \text{m}$, so the size is $6 \times 10^{17} \, \text{m}$, and the size in AU is $6 \times 10^{17}/(1.5 \times 10^{11}) \, \text{AU} = 4 \times 10^6 \, \text{AU}$.

SAQ 3.7

The diameter $2R$ of the AGN is less than or equal to the distance that light can travel in the time t of the variations. From Equation 3.4, $2R = ct = (3 \times 10^8 \, \text{m s}^{-1}) \times (3\,600 \, \text{s}) = 1.1 \times 10^{12} \, \text{m} = 1.1 \times 10^{12}/(3 \times 10^{16}) \, \text{pc} = 4 \times 10^{-5} \, \text{pc}$. Infrared radiation usually comes from dust surrounding the AGN. It has larger dimensions, and therefore the time-scale for variations is longer.

SAQ 3.8

By the inverse square law, the AGN is $(2\,000/50)^2$ times brighter than the 50 Mpc galaxy in the optical. Therefore, given that a galaxy like our own emits mostly in the optical, the luminosity is about $3 \times (2\,000/50)^2 = 4\,800$ times the luminosity of our galaxy, namely about $10^{14}L_\odot$. [*Comment*: This ignores redshift and absorption effects on the spectrum.]

SAQ 3.9

For the Seyfert nucleus, $L = 4 \times 10^{10}L_\odot = 1.6 \times 10^{37} \, \text{W}$. By Equation 3.6, $Q = L/(0.1c^2)$. Substituting for L,

$$Q = \frac{1.6 \times 10^{37}}{(0.1 \times 9 \times 10^{16})} \, \text{kg s}^{-1} \approx 2 \times 10^{21} \, \text{kg s}^{-1}$$

Converting into solar masses per year, and using $1 \, \text{yr} = 3 \times 10^7 \, \text{s}$, and $M_\odot = 2 \times 10^{30} \, \text{kg}$, gives

$$Q = \frac{2 \times 10^{21} \times 3 \times 10^7}{2 \times 10^{30}} M_\odot \, \text{yr}^{-1} \approx 0.03 M_\odot \, \text{yr}^{-1}$$

The Eddington limit places an upper limit on the luminosity for a black hole of given mass.

SAQ 3.10

From Equation 2.2 (and Figure 3.34), $z = 0.20$ corresponds to a distance of 800 Mpc. Using the inverse square law, the quasar must be $(800/200)^2$ times as luminous as the galaxy in order that both appear to have the same optical brightness from Earth. So the answer is 16.

SAQ 3.11

Reading from Figure 3.34, $z = 0.30$ corresponds to 1 170 Mpc, $z = 0.27$ to 1 070 Mpc, and $z = 0.23$ to 920 Mpc. Thus, 1 170 Mpc is the quasar distance. The objects causing the absorption lines must contain gas, and are most likely to be spiral or irregular galaxies. The distances to the galaxies are 1 070 Mpc and 920 Mpc. [*Comment*: Figure 3.34 shows that, at $z = 0.3$, there is a small but noticeable departure from the linear relationship in Equation 2.2, which gives 1 200 Mpc at $z = 0.3$.]

SAQ answers and comments for Chapter 4

SAQ 4.1

The Local Group is about 2 Mpc across. Light travels this distance in a time t given by

$$
\begin{aligned}
t \;&\approx\; 2\,\text{Mpc}/(3.0 \times 10^5\,\text{km s}^{-1}) \\
&\approx\; 6.7 \times 10^{-6}\ (\text{s Mpc/km}) \\
&\approx\; (6.7 \times 10^{-6}) \times (3.1 \times 10^{19})\,\text{s} \\
&\approx\; 2.1 \times 10^{14}\,\text{s} \\
&\approx\; 7\ \text{million years}
\end{aligned}
$$

Thus, the light we receive today from the members of the Local Group has been up to about half of the 7 million years travelling to us, because the Galaxy is near the centre of the Local Group (Figure 4.1), and so we see the members today as they were up to about 3 million years ago. The farther away the member, the further back in time we are now seeing it. [*Comment*: This is lookback time.]

SAQ 4.2

(i) The Virgo cluster is about 20 Mpc away. Thus, proceeding as in SAQ 4.1, we deduce that we see this cluster as it was about 70 million years ago – about 0.5% of the age of the Universe. (ii) The CfA survey extends out to about 200 Mpc, and so we see galaxies at this limit as they were about 700 million years ago – about 5% of the age of the Universe.

SAQ 4.3

We cannot necessarily conclude that all these galaxies belong to a single (rich) cluster because (i) the distances are unknown, so the galaxies might not all be close together, and (ii) even for those that are close to each other, they might not all be gravitationally bound together.

SAQ 4.4

(a) (i) The ball-bearings represent voids where galaxies are scarce. (ii) The air around them represents spaces where galaxies concentrate, in clusters, superclusters, filaments and sheets. (iii) The average ball-bearing diameter is the distance across the average void.

(b) The limitations of this model are: (i) it is unfortunate that mass concentration in the model (the ball-bearing) represents regions in the Universe where galaxies are scarce (voids); (ii) real voids are not all spherical, and consequently the shape of the actual regions where galaxies concentrate only crudely resembles the shape of the air-spaces in the model; (iii) the air-spaces in the model are homogeneous, with no hint of clusters, superclusters and other inhomogeneities in the spatial distribution of the galaxies.

SAQ 4.5

Galaxies that lie in the direction of the large-scale motion of the Local Group have redshifts that are reduced by the motion, whereas those that lie in the opposite direction have their redshifts increased. Those that lie in directions half-way between these extremes have their redshifts unaffected by the motion.

Acknowledgements

We are grateful to John Wilkinson, of the University of Central Queensland, for his helpful comments on a late draft of this book.

Grateful acknowledgement is also made to the following sources for permission to reproduce material in this book:

Chapter 1

Figure 1.3 The Observatories of the Carnegie Institute of Washington; *Figure 1.11* F. Combes (1991), 'Distribution of CO in the Milky Way', *Annual Review of Astronomy and Astrophysics*, vol. 29, pp. 195–237, reproduced, with permission, from the *Annual Review of Astronomy and Astrophysics*, vol. 29, copyright © 1991 by Annual Reviews Inc.; *Figure 1.16* Y. M. Georgelin and Y. P. Georgelin, Observatory of Marseille; *Figure 1.20* Courtesy of Dennis di Cicco; *Figures 1.25, 1.29* D. Mihalas and J. Binney (1981), *Galactic Astronomy*, copyright © 1981 by W. H. Freeman and Co., reprinted with permission; *Figure 1.27* Klaas de Boer and Blair Savage (1982), 'The Coronas of Galaxies', copyright © 1982 by Scientific American Inc., all rights reserved, illustration by Walken Graphics; *Figure 1.30* Adapted from L. Kühn (1982), *The Milky Way*, copyright © 1982 by John Wiley and Sons Ltd, reprinted by permission of John Wiley and Sons Ltd; *Figures 1.31, 1.33* Courtesy of Rheinhard Genzel, Max Planck Institut, Munich.

Chapter 2

Figures 2.1, 2.5 The Observatories of the Carnegie Institute of Washington; *Figures 2.4, 2.8* D. W. Sciama (1972) *Modern Cosmology*, Cambridge University Press, Pl. 7; *Figure 2.7* Halton C. Arp (1966) *Atlas of Peculiar Galaxies*, California Institute of Technology, courtesy of Caltech; *Figure 2.10* Bart J. Bok and Priscilla F. Bok (1974), reprinted by permission of the publishers from *The Milky Way*, Cambridge, Mass., Harvard University Press, copyright © 1941, 1945, 1957, 1974 by the President and Fellows of Harvard College; *Figure 2.12* R. Berendzen, R. Hart and D. Seeley (1976), *Man Discovers the Galaxies*, New York, Science History Publications; *Figure 2.13* Courtesy of Mount Palomar Observatory; *Figure 2.16* Adapted from A. Sandage (1970), *Physics Today*, vol. 34, February 1970, American Institute of Physics; *Figure 2.20* D. Mihalas and J. Binney (1968) *Galactic Astronomy*, copyright © 1968 by W. H. Freeman and Co., reprinted with permission; *Figure 2.21* Adapted from H. Spinrad and M. Peimbert (1975), 'Spiral and gaseous content of galaxies', Sandage, A., Sandage, M. and Kristian, J. (eds), *Galaxies and the Universe*, University of Chicago Press; *Figure 2.23* Illustration by Johnny Johnson (1983), from 'How the Milky Way formed', by Sydney van den Burgh and James Hesser, *Scientific American*, January 1993, International Edition; *Figure 2.24* J. Binney and S. Tremaine (1987), *Galactic Dynamics*, Princeton University Press, Fig. 4.19, courtesy of T. S. van Albada; *Figure 2.25* Courtesy of Anglo-Australian Observatory, photography by David Malin; *Figure 2.26* P. J. Quinn (1984), 'On the formation and dynamics of shells around elliptical galaxies', *Astrophysical Journal*, vol. 279, pp. 596–609, Figs 1–4, reprinted with permission from the *Astrophysical Journal*.

Chapter 3

Figures 3.1, 3.12 Robert C. Kennicut, Jr. (1992), Spectra of four Galactic stars, from 'A spectrophotometric atlas of galaxies', *Astrophysical Journal Supplement*, vol. 79 no. 2, pp. 255–284; *Figures 3.6, 3.19* From *Le Grand Atlas de L'Astronomie*, 1983, 1986, by permission of Encyclopaedia Universalis; *Figure 3.13* Reproduced with permission, from the *Annual Review of Astronomy and Astrophysics*, vol. 26, copyright © 1988, by Annual Reviews Inc.; *Figures*

Index